Certificate in Business Accounting

Paper C3

Business Mathematics

ASSESSMENT KIT

CIMA

FTC Foulks Lynch
A **Kaplan Professional** Company

British Library Cataloguing-in-Publication Data

A catalogue record for this book is available from the British Library.

Published by FTC Foulks Lynch
Swift House
Market Place
Wokingham
Berkshire
RG40 1AP

ISBN 1 84390 462 4

© The Financial Training Company Ltd, 2005

Printed and bound in Great Britain

Acknowledgements

We are grateful to the Chartered Institute of Management Accountants, the Association of Chartered Certified Accountants and the Institute of Chartered Accountants in England and Wales for permission to reproduce past examination questions. The answers have been prepared by FTC Foulks Lynch.

INTRODUCTION

We have worked closely with experienced CIMA tutors and lecturers to ensure that our Kits are assessment-focused and user-friendly.

This Assessment Kit includes an extensive selection of questions that entirely cover the syllabus – this ensures that your knowledge is tested across all syllabus areas. All questions in the Kit are grouped by syllabus topics with separate sections for 'objective test questions' and 'practice questions'

Questions are of assessment standard and format – this enables you to master the assessment techniques.

There is a mock at the back of the book – try it under timed conditions and this will give you an exact idea of the way you will be tested in your assessment.

CONTENTS

Section

INDEX TO QUESTIONS AND ANSWERS

SYLLABUS AND LEARNING OUTCOMES

Syllabus overview

This is a Foundation Level study in mathematical and statistical concepts and techniques. The first two sections, Basic Mathematics and Summarising and Analysing Data, include techniques which are fundamental to the work of the Chartered Management Accountant. The third section covers basic probability and is needed because Chartered Management Accountants need to be aware of and be able to estimate the risk and uncertainty involved in the decisions they make. The fourth section is an introduction to financial mathematics, a topic that is important to the study of financial management. Finally, there is an introduction to the mathematical techniques needed for forecasting, necessary in the area of business planning.

Aim

This syllabus aims to test the student's ability to:

- explain and demonstrate the use of basic mathematics, including formulae and ratios;

- identify reasonableness in the calculation of answers;

- identify and apply techniques for summarising and analysing data;

- explain and demonstrate the use of probability where risk and uncertainty exist;

- explain and apply financial mathematical techniques;

- explain and demonstrate techniques used for forecasting.

Learning outcomes and syllabus content

Basic mathematics – 10%

Learning outcomes

On completion of their studies students should be able to:

- demonstrate the order of operations in formulae, including the use of brackets, negative numbers, powers and roots;

- calculate percentages and proportions;

- calculate answers to appropriate significant figures or decimal places;

- calculate maximum absolute and relative errors;

- solve simple equations, including two variable simultaneous equations and quadratic equations;

- prepare graphs of linear and quadratic equations;

Syllabus content

- Use of formulae.
- Percentages and ratios.
- Rounding of numbers.
- Basic algebraic techniques and the solution of equations, including simultaneous and quadratic equations.

Summarising and analysing data – 25%Learning outcomes

On completion of their studies students should be able to:

- explain the difference between data and information;
- explain the characteristics of good information;
- explain the difference between primary and secondary data;
- identify the sources of secondary data;
- explain the different methods of sampling and identify where each is appropriate;
- tabulate data and explain the results;
- prepare a frequency distribution from raw data;
- prepare and explain the following graphs and diagrams: bar charts, time series graphs (not Z charts), scatter diagrams, histograms and ogives;
- calculate and explain the following summary statistics for ungrouped data: arithmetic mean, median, mode, range, standard deviation and variance;
- calculate and explain the following summary statistics for grouped data: arithmetic mean, median (graphical method only), mode (graphical method only), range, semi-interquartile range (graphical method only), standard deviation and variance;
- calculate and explain a simple index number, a fixed base and chain base series of index numbers;
- use index numbers to deflate a series and explain the results;
- calculate a simple weighted index number. Candidates will not have to decide whether to use base or current weights.

Syllabus content

- Data and information.
- Primary and secondary data.
- Probability sampling (simple random sampling, stratified, systematic, multi-stage, cluster) and non-profitability sampling (quota).
- Tabulation of data.
- Frequency distributions.
- Graphs and diagrams: bar charts, time series graphs (not Z charts), scatter diagrams, histograms and ogives.
- Summary measures for both grouped and ungrouped data.
- Coefficient of variation.
- Index numbers.

Probability – 20%

Learning outcomes

On completion of their studies students should be able to:

- calculate a simple probability;
- demonstrate the use of the addition and multiplication rules of probability;
- calculate a simple conditional probability;
- calculate and explain an expected value;
- demonstrate the use of expected values to make decisions;
- explain the limitations of expected values;
- demonstrate the use of normal distribution and the CIMA Tables;
- demonstrate the application of the normal distribution to calculate probabilities

Syllabus content

- The relationship between probability, proportion and per cent.
- The addition and multiplication rules.
- Expected values.
- Normal distribution.

Financial Mathematics – 20%

Learning outcomes

- calculate future values of an investment, using both simple and compound interest;
- calculate an annual percentage rate of interest, given a quarterly or monthly rate;
- calculate the present value of a future cash sum, using both a formula and CIMA Tables;
- calculate the present value of an annuity using both a formula and CIMA Tables;
- calculate loan/mortgage repayments and the value of an outstanding loan/mortgage;
- calculate the present value of a perpetuity;
- calculate the future value of regular savings (sinking funds) or find the savings given the future value, if necessary, using the sum of a geometric progression;
- calculate the NPV of a project and use this to decide whether a project should be undertaken, or to choose between mutually exclusive projects;

Syllabus content

- Simple and compound interest.
- Discounting to find the present value.
- Annuities and perpetuities.
- Loans and mortgages.
- Sinking funds and savings funds.
- Simple investment appraisal.

Forecasting – 25%

Learning outcomes

On completion of their studies students should be able to:

- calculate the correlation coefficient between two variables and explain the value;

- calculate the rank correlation coefficient between two sets of data and explain the value;

- explain the meaning of $100r^2$ (the coefficient of determination);

- demonstrate the use of regression analysis between two variables to find the line of best fit, and explain its meaning;

- calculate a forecast of the value of the dependent variable, given the value of the independent variable;

- prepare a time series graph and identify trends and patterns;

- identify the components of a time series model;

- calculate the trend using a graph, moving averages or linear regression, and be able to forecast the trend;

- calculate the seasonal variations for both additive and multiplicative models;

- calculate a forecast of the actual value using either the additive or the multiplicative model;

- explain the difference between the additive and multiplicative models, and when each is appropriate;

- calculate the seasonally adjusted values in a time series;

- explain the reliability of any forecasts made

Syllabus content

- Correlation.

- Simple linear regression.

- Time series analysis – graphical analysis.

- Calculation of trend using graphs, moving averages and linear regression.

- Seasonal variations – additive and multiplicative.

- Forecasting.

REVISION GUIDANCE

Planning your revision

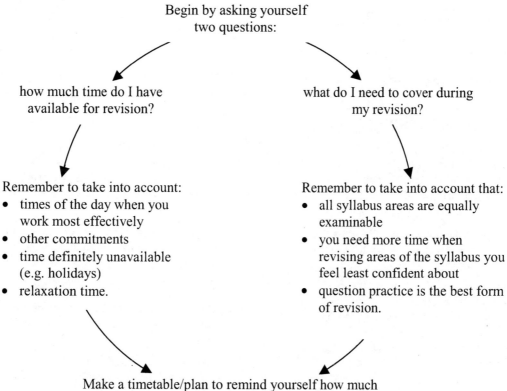

Begin by asking yourself
two questions:

how much time do I have
available for revision?

what do I need to cover during
my revision?

Remember to take into account:
- times of the day when you
  work most effectively
- other commitments
- time definitely unavailable
  (e.g. holidays)
- relaxation time.

Remember to take into account that:
- all syllabus areas are equally
  examinable
- you need more time when
  revising areas of the syllabus you
  feel least confident about
- question practice is the best form
  of revision.

Make a timetable/plan to remind yourself how much
work you have to do and when you are free to do it.
Allow some time for slippage.

Revision techniques

- Go through your notes and textbook **highlighting the important points**

- You might want to produce your own set of **summarised notes**

- **List key words** for each topic to remind you of the essential concepts

- **Practice assessment-standard questions**, under timed conditions

- **Rework questions** that you got completely wrong the first time, but only when you think
  you know the subject better

- If you get stuck on topics, **find someone to explain** them to you (your tutor or a colleague,
  for example)

- **Read recent articles** on the CIMA website and in *Insider*

- **Read** good newspapers and professional journals.

COMPUTER BASED ASSESSMENT

Format of the assessment

35 objective test questions

Total time allowed: 90 minutes

Number of marks
100

About the assessment

- The process for entering for a Computer Based Assessment (CBA) is different from entering for a paper based exam.

- Contact CIMA or look up on the CIMA website to find out where your nearest CIMA accredited CBA centre is. Contact the centre and arrange to sit the assessment.

- With CBAs the most common type of questions is 'multiple choice', where you have to choose the correct answer from a list of possible answers, but there are a variety of other **objective question types** that can be used within the system. These include true/false questions, matching pairs of text and graphic, sequencing and ranking, labelling diagrams and single and multiple numeric entry. There are also questions that carry several marks.

- You need to be sure you **know how to answer questions** of this type before you sit the assessment. You will achieve this through practice.

- Whatever the format, these questions require that you have *learnt* definitions, *know* key words and their meanings and importance, and *understand* the names and meanings of rules, concepts and theories.

- Do not attempt a CBA until you have **completed all study material** relating to it.

- **Do not skip any of the material** in the syllabus.

- Before you start the assessment make sure you understand how to use the **software**. If in doubt, ask the assessment centre staff to explain it to you.

- With CBAs, questions are **displayed on the screen** and answers are entered using keyboard and mouse.

- **Read each question** *very* carefully.

- **Double-check your answer** before committing yourself to it.

- If you are answering a multiple-choice question, eliminate first those answers that you know are definitely wrong. Then choose the most appropriate answer from those that are left.

- Remember that **only one answer to a multiple-choice question can be right**.

- Answer *every* question – if you do not know an answer, you don't lose anything by guessing. Think carefully before you **guess**.

- **Don't panic** if you realise you've answered a question incorrectly – you can always go back and change your answer.

- At the end of the assessment, you are given a **certificate showing the result** you have achieve.

MATHEMATICAL TABLES AND FORMULAE

Logarithms

	0	1	2	3	4	5	6	7	8	9	1	2	3	4	5	6	7	8	9
10	0000	0043	0086	0128	0170						4	9	13	17	21	26	30	34	38
						0212	0253	0294	0334	0374	4	8	12	16	20	24	28	32	37
11	0414	0453	0492	0531	0569						4	8	12	15	19	23	27	31	35
						0607	0645	0682	0719	0755	4	7	11	15	19	22	26	30	33
12	0792	0828	0864	0899	0934	0969					3	7	11	14	18	21	25	28	32
							1004	1038	1072	1106	3	7	10	14	17	20	24	27	31
13	1139	1173	1206	1239	1271						3	7	10	13	16	20	23	26	30
						1303	1335	1367	1399	1430	3	7	10	12	16	19	22	25	29
14	1461	1492	1523	1553							3	6	9	12	15	18	21	24	28
					1584	1614	1644	1673	1703	1732	3	6	9	12	15	17	20	23	26
15	1761	1790	1818	1847	1875	1903					3	6	9	11	14	17	20	23	26
							1931	1959	1987	2014	3	5	8	11	14	16	19	22	25
16	2041	2068	2095	2122	2148						3	5	8	11	14	16	19	22	24
						2175	2201	2227	2253	2279	3	5	8	10	13	15	18	21	23
17	2304	2330	2355	2380	2405	2430					3	5	8	10	13	15	18	20	23
							2455	2480	2504	2529	2	5	7	10	12	15	17	19	22
18	2553	2577	2601	2625	2648						2	5	7	9	12	14	16	19	21
						2672	2695	2718	2742	2765	2	5	7	9	11	14	16	18	21
19	2788	2810	2833	2856	2878						2	4	7	9	11	13	16	18	20
						2900	2923	2945	2967	2989	2	4	6	8	11	13	15	17	19
20	3010	3032	3054	3075	3096	3118	3139	3160	3181	3201	2	4	6	8	11	13	15	17	19
21	3222	3243	3263	3284	3304	3324	3345	3365	3385	3404	2	4	6	8	10	12	14	16	18
22	3424	3444	3464	3483	3502	3522	3541	3560	3579	3598	2	4	6	8	10	12	14	15	17
23	3617	3636	3655	3674	3692	3711	3729	3747	3766	3784	2	4	6	7	9	11	13	15	17
24	3802	3820	3838	3856	3874	3892	3909	3927	3945	3962	2	4	5	7	9	11	12	14	16
25	3979	3997	4014	4031	4048	4065	4082	4099	4116	4133	2	3	5	7	9	10	12	14	15
26	4150	4166	4183	4200	4216	4232	4249	4265	4281	4298	2	3	5	7	8	10	11	13	15
27	4314	4330	4346	4362	4378	4393	4409	4425	4440	4456	2	3	5	6	8	9	11	13	14
28	4472	4487	4502	4518	4533	4548	4564	4579	4594	4609	2	3	5	6	8	9	11	12	14
29	4624	4639	4652	4669	4683	4698	4713	4728	4742	4757	1	3	4	6	7	9	10	12	13
30	4771	4786	4800	4814	4829	4843	4857	4871	4886	4900	1	3	4	6	7	9	10	11	13
31	4914	4928	4942	4955	4969	4983	4997	5011	5024	5038	1	3	4	6	7	8	10	11	12
32	5051	5065	5079	5092	5105	5119	5132	5145	5159	5172	1	3	4	5	7	8	9	11	12
33	5185	5198	5211	5224	5237	5250	5263	5276	5289	5302	1	3	4	5	6	8	9	10	12
34	5315	5328	5340	5353	5366	5378	5391	5403	5416	5428	1	3	4	5	6	8	9	10	11
35	5441	5453	5465	5478	5490	5502	5514	5527	5539	5551	1	2	4	5	6	7	9	10	11
36	5563	5575	5587	5599	5611	5623	5635	5647	5658	5670	1	2	4	5	6	7	8	10	11
37	5682	5694	5705	5717	5729	5740	5752	5763	5775	5786	1	2	3	5	6	7	8	9	10
38	5798	5809	5821	5932	5843	5855	5866	5877	5888	5899	1	2	3	5	6	7	8	9	10
39	5911	5922	5933	5944	5955	5966	5977	5988	5999	6010	1	2	3	4	5	7	8	9	10
40	6021	6031	6042	6053	6064	6075	6085	6096	6107	6117	1	2	3	4	5	6	8	9	10
41	6128	6138	6149	6160	6170	6180	6191	6201	6212	6222	1	2	3	4	5	6	7	8	9
42	6232	6243	6253	6263	6274	6284	6294	6304	6314	6325	1	2	3	4	5	6	7	8	9
43	6335	6345	6355	6365	6375	6385	6395	6405	6415	6425	1	2	3	4	5	6	7	8	9
44	6435	6444	6454	6464	6474	6484	6493	6503	6513	6522	1	2	3	4	5	6	7	8	9
45	6532	6542	6551	6561	6571	6580	6590	9599	6609	6618	1	2	3	4	5	6	7	8	9
46	6628	6637	6646	6656	6665	6675	6684	6693	6702	6712	1	2	3	4	5	6	7	7	8
47	6721	6730	6739	6749	6758	6767	6776	6785	6794	6803	1	2	3	4	5	5	6	7	8
48	6812	6821	6830	6839	6848	6857	6866	6875	6884	6893	1	2	3	4	4	5	6	7	8
49	6902	6911	6920	6928	6937	6946	6955	6964	6972	6981	1	2	3	4	4	5	6	7	8

Logarithms

	0	1	2	3	4	5	6	7	8	9	1	2	3	4	5	6	7	8	9
50	6990	6998	7007	7016	7024	7033	7042	7050	7059	7067	1	2	3	3	4	5	6	7	8
51	7076	7084	7093	7101	7110	7118	7126	7135	7143	7152	1	2	3	3	4	5	6	7	8
52	7160	7168	7177	7185	7193	7202	7210	7218	7226	7235	1	2	2	3	4	5	6	7	7
53	7243	7251	7259	7267	7275	7284	7292	7300	7308	7316	1	2	2	3	4	5	6	6	7
54	7324	7332	7340	7348	7356	7364	7372	7380	7388	7396	1	2	2	3	4	5	6	6	7
55	7404	7412	7419	7427	7435	7443	7451	7459	7466	7474	1	2	2	3	4	5	5	6	7
56	7482	7490	7497	7505	7513	7520	7528	7536	7543	7551	1	2	2	3	4	5	5	6	7
57	7559	7566	7574	7582	7589	7597	7604	7612	7619	7627	1	2	2	3	4	5	5	6	7
58	7634	7642	7649	7657	7664	7672	7679	7686	7694	7701	1	1	2	3	4	4	5	6	7
59	7709	7716	7723	7731	7738	7745	7752	7760	7767	7774	1	1	2	3	4	4	5	6	7
60	7782	7789	7796	7803	7810	7818	7825	7832	7839	7846	1	1	2	3	4	4	5	6	6
61	7853	7860	7868	7875	7882	7889	7896	7903	7910	7917	1	1	2	3	4	4	5	6	6
62	7924	7931	7938	7945	7952	7959	7966	7973	7980	7987	1	1	2	3	3	4	5	6	6
63	7993	8000	8007	8014	8021	8028	8035	8041	8048	8055	1	1	2	3	3	4	5	5	6
64	8062	8069	9075	8082	8089	8096	8102	8109	8116	8122	1	1	2	3	3	4	5	5	6
65	8129	8136	8142	8149	8156	8162	8169	8176	8182	8189	1	1	2	3	3	4	5	5	6
66	8195	8202	8209	8215	8222	8228	8235	8241	8248	8254	1	1	2	3	3	4	5	5	6
67	8261	8267	8274	8280	8287	8293	8299	8306	8312	8319	1	1	2	3	3	4	5	5	6
68	8325	8331	8338	8344	8351	8357	8363	8370	8376	8382	1	1	2	3	3	4	4	5	6
69	8388	8395	8401	8407	8414	8420	8426	8432	8439	8445	1	1	2	2	3	4	4	5	6
70	8451	8457	8463	8470	8476	8482	8488	8494	8500	8506	1	1	2	2	3	4	4	5	6
71	8513	8519	8525	8531	8537	8543	8549	8555	8561	8567	1	1	2	2	3	4	4	5	5
72	8573	8579	8585	8591	8597	8603	8609	8615	8621	8627	1	1	2	2	3	4	4	5	5
73	8633	8639	8645	8651	8657	8663	8669	8675	8681	8686	1	1	2	2	3	4	4	5	5
74	8692	8698	8704	8710	8716	8722	8727	8733	8739	8745	1	1	2	2	3	4	4	5	5
75	8751	8756	8762	8768	8774	8779	8785	8791	8797	8802	1	1	2	2	3	3	4	5	5
76	8808	8814	8820	8825	8831	8837	8842	8848	8854	8859	1	1	2	2	3	3	4	5	5
77	8865	8871	8876	8882	8887	8893	8899	8904	8910	8915	1	1	2	2	3	3	4	4	5
78	8921	8927	8932	8938	8943	8949	8954	8960	8965	8971	1	1	2	2	3	3	4	4	5
79	8976	8982	8987	8993	8998	9004	9009	9015	9020	9025	1	1	2	2	3	3	4	4	5
80	9031	9036	9042	9047	9053	9058	9063	9069	9074	9079	1	1	2	2	3	3	4	4	5
81	9085	9090	9096	9101	9106	9112	9117	9122	9128	9133	1	1	2	2	3	3	4	4	5
82	9138	9143	9149	9154	9159	9165	9170	9175	9180	9186	1	1	2	2	3	3	4	4	5
83	9191	9196	9201	9206	9212	9217	9222	9227	9232	9238	1	1	2	2	3	3	4	4	5
84	9243	9248	9253	9258	9263	9269	9274	9279	9284	9289	1	1	2	2	3	3	4	4	5
85	9294	9299	9304	9309	9315	9320	9325	9330	9335	9340	1	1	2	2	3	3	4	4	5
86	9345	9350	8355	9360	9365	9370	9375	9380	9385	9390	1	1	2	2	3	3	4	4	5
87	9395	9400	9405	9410	9415	9420	9425	9430	9435	9440	0	1	1	2	2	3	3	4	5
88	9445	9450	9455	9460	9465	9469	9474	9479	9484	9489	0	1	1	2	2	3	3	4	5
89	9494	9499	9504	9509	9513	9518	9523	9528	9533	9538	0	1	1	2	2	3	3	4	5
90	9542	9547	9552	9557	9562	9566	9571	9576	9581	9586	0	1	1	2	2	3	3	4	4
91	9590	9595	9600	9605	9609	9614	9619	9624	9628	9633	0	1	1	2	2	3	3	4	4
92	9638	9643	9647	9652	9657	9661	9666	9671	9675	9680	0	1	1	2	2	3	3	4	4
93	9685	9689	9594	9699	9703	9708	9713	9717	9722	9727	0	1	1	2	2	3	3	4	4
94	9731	9736	9741	9745	9750	9754	9759	9763	9768	9773	0	1	1	2	2	3	3	4	4
95	9777	9782	9786	9791	9795	9800	9805	9809	9814	9818	0	1	1	2	2	3	3	4	4
96	9823	9827	9832	9836	9841	9845	9850	9854	9859	9863	0	1	1	2	2	3	3	4	4
97	9868	9872	9877	9881	9886	9890	9894	9899	9903	9908	0	1	1	2	2	3	3	4	4
98	9911	9917	9921	9926	9930	9934	9939	9943	9948	9952	0	1	1	2	2	3	3	4	4
99	9956	9961	9965	9969	9974	9978	9983	9987	9991	9996	0	1	1	2	2	3	3	3	4

Area under the normal curve

This table gives the area under the normal curve between the mean and a point Z standard deviations above the mean. The corresponding area for deviations below the mean can be found by symmetry.

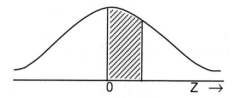

$Z=\dfrac{(x-\mu)}{\sigma}$	0.00	0.01	0.02	0.03	0.04	0.05	0.06	0.07	0.08	0.09
	.0000	.0040	.0080	.0120	.0159	.0199	.0239	.0279	.0319	.0359
0.0	.0398	.0438	.0478	.0517	.0557	.0596	.0636	.0675	.0714	.0753
0.1	.0793	.0832	.0871	.0910	.0948	.0987	.1026	.1064	.1103	.1141
0.2	.1179	.1217	.1255	.1293	.1331	.1368	.1406	.1443	.1408	.1517
0.3	.1554	.1591	.1628	.1664	.1700	.1736	.1772	.1808	.1844	.1879
0.4										
0.5	.1915	.1950	.1985	.2019	.2054	.2088	.2123	.2157	.2190	.2224
0.6	.2257	.2291	.2324	.2357	.2389	.2422	.2454	.2486	.2518	.2549
0.7	.2580	.2611	.2642	.2673	.2704	.2734	.2764	.2794	.2823	.2852
0.8	.2881	.2910	.2939	.2967	.2995	.3023	.3051	.3078	.3106	.3133
0.9	.3159	.3186	.3212	.3238	.3264	.3289	.3315	.3340	.3365	.3389
1.0	.3413	.3438	.3461	.3485	.3508	.3531	.3554	.3577	.3599	.3621
1.1	.3643	.3665	.3686	.3708	.3729	.3749	.3770	.3790	.3810	.3830
1.2	.3849	.3869	.3888	.3907	.3925	.3944	.3962	.3980	.3997	.4015
1.3	.4032	.4049	.4066	.4082	4099	.4115	.4131	.4147	.4162	.4177
1.4	.4192	.4207	.4222	.4236	.4251	.4265	.4279	.4292	.4306	.4319
1.5	.4332	.4345	.4357	.4370	.4382	.4394	.4406	.4418	.4430	.4441
1.6	.4452	.4463	.4474	.4485	.4495	.4505	.4515	.4525	.4535	.4545
1.7	.4554	.4564	.4573	.4582	.4591	.4599	.4608	.4616	.4625	.4633
1.8	.4641	.4649	.4656	.4664	.4671	.4678	.4686	.4693	.4699	.4706
1.9	.4713	.4719	.4726	.4732	.4738	.4744	.4750	.4756	.4762	.4767
2.0	.4772	.4778	.4783	.4788	.4793	.4798	.4803	.4808	.4812	.4817
2.1	.4821	.4826	.4830	.4834	.4838	.4842	.4846	.4850	.4854	.4857
2.2	.4861	.4865	.4868	.4871	.4875	.4878	.4881	.4884	.4887	.4890
2.3	.4893	.4896	.4898	.4901	.4904	.4906	.4909	.4911	.4913	.4916
2.4	.4918	.4920	.4922	.4925	.4927	.4929	.4931	.4932	.4934	.4936
2.5	.4938	.4940	.4941	.4943	.4945	.4946	.4948	.4949	.4951	.4952
2.6	.4953	.4955	.4956	.4957	.4959	.4960	.4961	.4962	4963	.4964
2.7	.4965	.4966	.4967	.4968	.4969	.4970	.4971	.4972	.4973	.4974
2.8	.4974	.4975	.4976	.4977	.4977	.4978	.4979	.4980	.4980	.4981
2.9	.4981	.4982	.4983	.4983	.4984	.4984	.4985	.4985	.4986	.4986
3.0	**.49865**	.4987	.4987	.4988	.4988	.4989	.4989	.4989	.4990	.4990
3.1	**.49903**	.4991	.4991	.4991	.4992	.4992	.4992	.4992	.4993	.4993
3.2	**.49931**	.4993	.4994	.4994	.4994	.4994	.4994	.4995	.4995	.4995
3.3	**.49952**	.4995	.4995	.4996	.4996	.4996	.4996	.4996	.4996	.4997
3.4	**.49966**	.4997	.4997	.4997	.4997	.4997	.4997	.4997	.4997	.4998
3.5	**.49977**									

Present value table

Present value of £1 i.e. $(1 + r)^{-n}$ where r = interest rate, n = number of periods until payment or receipt.

Periods	Interest rates (r)									
(n)	1%	2%	3%	4%	5%	6%	7%	8%	9%	10%
1	.990	.980	.971	.962	.962	.943	.935	.926	.917	.909
2	.980	.961	.943	.925	.907	.890	.873	.857	.842	.826
3	.971	.942	.915	.889	.864	.840	.816	.794	.772	.751
4	.961	.924	.888	.855	.823	.792	.763	.735	.708	.683
5	.951	.906	.863	.822	.784	.747	.713	.681	.650	.621
6	.942	.888	.837	.790	.746	.705	.666	.630	.596	.564
7	.933	.871	.813	.760	.711	.665	.623	.583	.547	.513
8	.923	.853	.789	.731	.677	.627	.582	.540	.502	.467
9	.914	.837	.766	.703	.645	.592	.544	.500	.460	.424
10	.905	.820	.744	.676	.614	.558	.508	.463	.422	.386
11	.896	.804	.722	.650	.585	.527	.475	.429	.388	.350
12	.887	.788	.701	.625	.557	.497	.444	.397	.356	.319
13	.879	.773	.681	.601	.530	.469	.415	.368	.326	.290
14	.870	.758	.661	.577	.505	.442	.388	.340	.299	.263
15	.861	.743	.642	.555	.481	.417	.362	.315	.275	.239
16	.853	.728	.623	.534	.458	.394	.339	.292	.252	.218
17	.844	.714	.605	.513	.436	.371	.317	.270	.231	.198
18	.836	.700	.587	.494	.416	.350	.296	.250	.212	.180
19	.828	.686	.570	.475	.396	.331	.277	.232	.194	.164
20	.820	.673	.554	.456	.377	.312	.258	.215	.178	.149

Periods	Interest rates (r)									
(n)	11%	12%	13%	14%	15%	16%	17%	18%	19%	20%
1	.901	.893	.885	.877	.870	.862	.855	.847	.840	.833
2	.812	.797	.783	.769	.756	.743	.731	.718	.706	.694
3	.731	.712	.693	.675	.658	.641	.624	.609	.593	.579
4	.659	.636	.613	.592	.572	.552	.534	.516	.499	.482
5	.593	.567	.543	.519	.497	.476	.456	.437	.419	.402
6	.535	.507	.480	.456	.432	.410	.390	.370	.352	.335
7	.482	.452	.425	.400	.376	.354	.333	.314	.296	.279
8	.434	.404	.376	.351	.327	.305	.285	.266	.249	.233
9	.391	.361	.333	.308	.284	.263	.243	.225	.209	.194
10	.352	.322	.295	.270	.247	.227	.208	.191	.176	.162
11	.317	.287	.261	.237	.215	.195	.178	.162	.148	.135
12	.286	.257	.231	.208	.187	.168	.152	.137	.124	.112
13	.258	.229	.204	.182	.163	.145	.130	.116	.104	.093
14	.232	.205	.181	.160	.141	.125	.111	.099	.088	.078
15	.209	.183	.160	.140	.123	.108	.095	.084	.074	.065
16	.188	.163	.141	.123	.107	.093	.081	.071	.062	.054
17	.170	.146	.125	.108	.093	.080	.069	.060	.052	.045
18	.153	.130	.111	.095	.081	.069	.059	.051	.044	.038
19	.138	.116	.098	.083	.070	.060	.051	.043	.037	.031
20	.124	.104	.087	.073	.061	.051	.043	.037	.031	.026

Cumulative present value of £1

This table shows the Present Value of £1 per annum, Receivable or Payable at the end of each year for n years

$$\frac{1-(1+r)^{-n}}{r}$$

Periods	Interest rates (r)									
(n)	1%	2%	3%	4%	5%	6%	7%	8%	9%	10%
1	0.990	0.980	0.971	0.962	0.952	0.943	0.935	0.926	0.917	0.909
2	1.970	1.942	1.913	1.886	1.859	1.833	1.808	1.783	1.759	1.736
3	2.941	2.884	2.829	2.775	2.723	2.673	2.624	2.577	2.531	2.487
4	3.902	3.808	3.717	3.630	3.546	3.465	3.387	3.312	3.240	3.170
5	4.853	4.713	4.580	4.452	4.329	4.212	4.100	3.993	3.890	3.791
6	5.795	5.601	5.417	5.242	5.076	4.917	4.767	4.623	4.486	4.355
7	6.728	6.472	6.230	6.002	5.786	5.582	5.389	5.206	5.033	4.868
8	7.652	7.325	7.020	6.733	6.463	6.210	5.971	5.747	5.535	5.335
9	8.566	8.162	7.786	7.435	7.108	6.802	6.515	6.247	5.995	5.759
10	9.471	8.983	8.530	8.111	7.722	7.360	7.024	6.710	6.418	6.145
11	10.368	9.787	9.253	8.760	8.306	7.887	7.499	7.139	6.805	8.495
12	11.255	10.575	9.954	9.385	8.863	8.384	7.943	7.536	7.161	6.814
13	12.134	11.348	10.635	9.986	9.394	8.853	8.358	7.904	7.487	7.103
14	13.004	12.106	11.296	10.563	9.899	9.295	8.745	8.244	7.786	7.367
15	13.865	12.849	11.938	11.118	10.380	9.712	9.108	8.559	8.061	7.606
16	14.718	13.578	12.561	11.652	10.838	10.106	9.447	8.851	8.313	7.824
17	15.562	14.292	13.166	12.166	11.274	10.477	9.763	9.122	8.544	8.022
18	16.398	14.992	13.754	12.659	11.690	10.828	10.059	9.372	8.756	8.201
19	17.226	15.679	14.324	13.134	12.085	11.158	10.336	9.604	8.950	8.365
20	18.046	16.351	14.878	13.590	12.462	11.470	10.594	9.818	9.129	8.514

Periods	Interest rates (r)									
(n)	11%	12%	13%	14%	15%	16%	17%	18%	19%	20%
1	0.901	0.893	0.885	0.877	0.870	0.862	0685	0.847	0.840	0.833
2	1.713	1.690	1.668	1.647	1.626	1.605	1.585	1.566	1.547	1.528
3	2.444	2.402	2.361	2.322	2.283	2.246	2.210	2.174	2.140	2.106
4	3.102	3.037	2.974	2.914	2.855	2.798	2.743	2.690	2.639	2.589
5	3.696	3.605	3.517	3.433	3.352	3.274	3.199	3.127	3.058	2.991
6	4.231	4.111	3.998	3.889	3.784	3.685	3.589	3.498	3.410	3.326
7	4.712	4.564	4.423	4.288	4.160	4.039	3.922	3.812	3.706	3.605
8	5.146	4.968	4.799	4.639	4.487	4.344	4.207	4.078	3.954	3.837
9	5.537	5.328	5.132	4.946	4.772	4.607	4.451	4.303	4.163	4.031
10	5.889	5.650	5.426	5.216	5.019	4.833	4.659	4.494	4.339	4.192
11	6.207	5.938	5.687	5.453	5.234	5.029	4.836	4.656	4.486	4.327
12	6.492	6.194	5.918	5.660	5.421	5.197	4.968	4.793	4.611	4.439
13	6.750	6.424	6.122	5.842	5.583	5.342	5.118	4.910	4.715	4.533
14	6.982	6.628	6.302	6.002	5.724	5.468	5.229	5.008	4.802	4.611
15	7.191	6.811	6.462	6.142	5.847	5.575	5.324	5.092	4.876	4.675
16	7.379	6.974	6.604	6.265	5.954	5.668	5.405	5.162	4.938	4.730
17	7.549	7.120	6.729	6.373	6.047	5.749	5.475	5.222	4.990	4.775
18	7.702	7.250	6.840	6.467	6.128	5.818	5.534	5.273	5.033	4.812
19	7.839	7.366	6.938	6.550	6.198	5.877	5.584	5.316	5.070	4.843
20	7.963	7.469	7.025	6.623	6.259	5.929	5.628	5.353	5.101	4.870

Formulae

Probability

$A \cup B$ = A or B. $A \cap B$ = A and B (overlap)

$P(B/A)$ = probability of B, given A.

Rules of Addition

If A and B are mutually exclusive: $\quad P(A \cup B) = P(A) + P(B)$

If A and B are not mutually exclusive: $\quad P(A \cup B) = P(A) + P(B) - P(A \cap B)$

Rules of Multiplication

If A and B are independent: $\quad P(A \cap B) = P(A)*P(B)$

If A and B are not independent: $\quad P(A \cap B) = P(A)*P(B/A)$

$E(X)$ = expected value = probability*payoff

Quadratic Equations

If $aX2 + bX + c = 0$ is the general quadratic equation, then the two solutions (roots) are given by:

$$X = \frac{-b \pm \sqrt{b^2 - 4ac}}{2a}$$

Descriptive statistics

Arithmetic Mean

$$\bar{x} = \frac{\Sigma x}{n} \text{ or } \bar{x} = \frac{\Sigma fx}{\Sigma f} \text{ (frequency distribution)}$$

Standard Deviation

$$SD = \sqrt{\frac{\Sigma(x - \bar{x})^2}{n}} \quad SD = \sqrt{\frac{\Sigma fx^2}{\Sigma f} - \bar{x}^2} \quad \text{(frequency distribution)}$$

Index numbers

Price relative = $100*P1/P0$ $\qquad$ Quantity relative = $100*Q1/Q0$

Price: $\Sigma W*P1/P0/\Sigma W*100$, where W denotes weights

Quantity: $\Sigma W*Q1/Q0/\Sigma W*100$, where W denotes weights

Time series

Additive Model

Series $\quad = \quad$ Trend + Seasonal + Random

Multiplicative Model

Series $\quad = \quad$ Trend * Seasonal * Random

Linear regression and correlation

The linear regression equation of Y on X is given by:

$$Y = a + bX \text{ or } Y - \overline{Y} = b(X - \overline{X})$$

where

$$b = \frac{\text{Covariance}(XY)}{\text{Variance}(X)} = \frac{n\Sigma\Sigma X - (\Sigma\Sigma X)(\Sigma Y}{n\Sigma\Sigma^2 - (\Sigma\Sigma X^2}$$

and

$$a = \overline{Y} - b\overline{X}$$

Or solve

$$\Sigma Y = na + b\Sigma X$$

$$\Sigma XY = a\Sigma X + b\Sigma X2$$

Coefficient of correlation

$$r = \frac{\text{Covariance}(XY)}{\sqrt{\text{Var}(X).\text{Var}(Y)}} = \frac{n\Sigma XY - (\Sigma X)(\Sigma Y)}{\sqrt{\{n\Sigma X^2 - (\Sigma X)^2\}\{n\Sigma Y^2 - (\Sigma Y)^2\}}}$$

$$R(\text{rank}) = 1 - \frac{6\Sigma d^2}{n(n^2 - 1)}$$

Financial mathematics

Compound Interest (Values and Sums)

Future value of S, of a sum X, inverted for n periods, compounded at r% interest

$$S = X[1 + r]n$$

Annuity

Present value of an annuity of £1 per annum receivable or payable for n years, commencing in one year, discounted at r% per annum:

$$PV = \frac{1}{r} - \left[1 - \frac{1}{[1+r]^n}\right]$$

Perpetuity

Present value of £1 per annum, payable or receivable in perpetuity, commencing in one year, discounted at r% per annum.

$$PV = \frac{1}{r}$$

Section 1

OBJECTIVE TEST QUESTIONS

BASIC MATHEMATICS

1   A product was previously sold for £2.60 per kg, but is now sold for £4 for 2 kgs. The percentage reduction per kg is closest to:

   A   21

   B   23

   C   25

   D   30

2   A jacket which cost the retailer £40 is sold at a profit of 20% on the selling price. The profit is therefore:

   A   £8

   B   £12

   C   £10

   D   £6

3   A retailer buys in a product for £50 per unit and wishes to achieve 40% gross profit on sales. The selling price per unit must be:

   A   £70.00

   B   £83.33

   C   £90.00

   D   £125.00

4   A person pays no tax on the first £3,500 of earnings and then 23% tax on the remainder of earnings. If he/she wishes to have £15,000 net of tax earnings, what gross earnings (to the nearest £) does he/she need?

   A   £15,000

   B   £18,435

   C   £18,500

   D   £19,481

5   To two decimal places, calculate the range of possible values for the expression $\frac{4.88}{0.8}$ where each term has been rounded.

A   6.00 to 6.10

B   5.74 to 6.51

C   0.8 to 4.88

D   0 to 4.88

6   The solution to the simultaneous equations $5x + 3y = 13$ and $3x - y = 12$ is:

A $x = 3.5;$ $y = -1.5$

B $x = 5.75;$ $y = -5.25$

C $x = 3.5;$ $y = 1.5$

D $x = 5.75;$ $y = 5.25$

7   A retailer buys a box of a product, which nominally contains Q units. The planned selling price of each unit is £P. If both P and Q have been rounded to ± 10%, then the maximum rounding error in total revenue is:

A   10%

B   20%

C   21%

D $0.1Q \times 0.1P$

8   The telephone costs of a company last year were £10,000, including Value Added Tax (VAT) at 17.5%. It has been decided to allocate 60% of these telephone costs, excluding VAT, to Central Administration and to allocate 30% of the remainder, excluding VAT, to Finance.

The telephone costs (to the nearest £) to be allocated to Finance will be closest to:

A   £990

B   £1,021

C   £1,100

D   £1,135

9   Two groups of stock, K and L, are valued. The first group, K, is valued at £10,000 ± 5% and the second group, L, is valued at £20,000 ± 10%.

The maximum percentage error in the combined (K + L) stock valuation of £30,000 is closest to:

A   7.5%

B   8.3%

C   10.0%

D   15.0%

10   A new lake is to be stocked with fish, according to the numbers in the table below.

Type of fish	A	B	C	D
Number of fish	400	300	200	100
Annual % increase	10	20	30	40

After one year, the percentage of fish of Type D in the lake will be closest to:

A   10%

B   12%

C   14%

D   20%

11   The fraction X^{10}/X^5 equals:

A   2

B   5

C X^2

D X^5

12   The price, P, of a product is planned to be £10, the quantity sold, Q, is expected to be 1,000 units, and the number of days trading, N, to be 10. If P, Q and N are each liable to an error of ± 10%, the minimum value of PQ/N (revenue per trading day) will be nearest to:

A   £675

B   £736

C   £900

D   £1,000

13   A company uses any one of three machines to produce 'identical' hinges. The output of hinges from the three machines is in the ratio 6:3:1. The percentage of defects is 5, 20 and 10 respectively. The overall percentage of defects is closest to:

A   8

B   9

C   10

D   11

14   A store sells oranges either for 39p per kg, or in bulk at £7 per 22 kg bag. The percentage saving (per kg) from buying a 22 kg bag is closest to:

A   7.2%

B   16.0%

C   18.4%

D   20.0%

15 If price per unit is estimated to within ± 20% and the quantity of units supplied to within ± 10%, then the maximum possible error in revenue is:

A   20%

B   28%

C   30%

D   32%

16 The total cost of servicing 1 million transactions was estimated at £10 million. The volume estimate has an error of ± ½% and the cost estimate ± 6%.

The minimum cost per transaction possible (to 2 decimal places) is:

A   £9.35

B   £9.45

C   £10.55

D   £10.65

17 A company's market for computer supplies has trebled in value in exactly six years. The annual equivalent percentage growth rate in this market is (to 2 decimal places) closest to:

A   12.25

B   20.09

C   24.57

D   33.33

18 A company's market value has fallen from £32 billion to £2 billion in four years. The average annual percentage decline in market value is closest to:

A   20%

B   40%

C   50%

D   100%

19 In the formula $Q = \sqrt{\frac{2CD}{H}}$, if C = £20, D = 24,000 and Q = 400, then H is closest in value to:

A   £2.45

B   £6.00

C   £12.00

D   £36.00

20   Rearranging the compound interest formula $S = \dfrac{A(R^2 - 1)}{(R - 1)}$, where $R \neq 1$, to make R the subject of the formula results in:

A $R = \dfrac{S}{A + 1}$

B $R = \dfrac{S}{A}$

C $R = \dfrac{S}{A} - 1$

D $R = \dfrac{1 - S}{A}$

21   In 1985 the annual value of retail sales in Great Britain was £8.792 × 10¹⁰. (Source: Economic Trends, January 1992). In 1991, this had risen by 53%. The value of retail sales in Great Britain in 1991 was closest to (in millions):

A   £13,452

B   £46,598

C   £134,518

D   £222,438

22   A piece of equipment is to be depreciated by the 'reducing balance' method, ie a constant percentage is applied to its written-down value after each year. It will cost £0.5 million and have an economic life of eight years, after which it will have a scrap value of £20,000. After one year its book value (in £000) will be closest to:

A   334

B   350

C   375

D   440

23   The following formula is used in the calculation of the value of savings:

Sr   = $R^N (Ar + P) - P$

Where A   = amount saved at the start,

       r   = rate of interest,

       N   = number of periods,

       P   = payments added each period,

       R   = $r + 1$

       S   = final sum.

If $r = 7\%$, $A = 3,000$, $N = 20$ and $P = 500$, then S equals (to the nearest £000):

A   30,000

B   31,000

C   32,000

D   33,000

24 A trader's total costs are made up of wages and materials. Next month wages are expected to be £1,000 ± 10% and materials £2,000 ± 20%. Revenue is predicted to be £4,000 ± 10%. Profit (revenue minus total costs) next month will be:

    A   between £100 and £900

    B   between £100 and £1,900

    C   £1,000 ± 10%

    D   £1,000 ± 20%

25 When x = 2, what is the value (to two decimal places) of the expression $\left(x^{-0.75}\right)^{-7}$?

    A   Zero

    B   0.03

    C   38.05

    D   64.26

26 The term $x^{-\frac{3}{4}}$ equals:

    A $\dfrac{1}{\sqrt[4]{x^3}}$

    B $\dfrac{3}{x^4}$

    C $\dfrac{1}{\sqrt[3]{x^4}}$

    D $\dfrac{4}{x^3}$

27 In the formula:

$$PV = \frac{1}{r} - \frac{1}{r(1+r)^n} \text{ , if r } = 0.05 \text{ and n} = 20, \text{ then PV equals:}$$

    A   12.10

    B   12.46

    C   19.62

    D   33.07

28 A machine was purchased for £100,000. Depreciation is calculated using the 'reducing balance method' (that is, a constant percentage is applied each year to the written down value). In the last balance sheet, the net book value of the machine, exactly four years old, was shown as £50,000.

In the next balance sheet the machine should be shown to have a net book value, rounded to the nearest £100, closest to:

A   £37,500

B   £40,000

C   £42,000

D   £43,500

29 The straight lines Y = 2X + 4 and Y = 12 − 2X intersect where (X,Y) equals:

A   (-2, 0)

B   (0, 12)

C   (0, 4)

D   (2, 8)

30 The following formula is used in loan calculations:

$$R = \frac{2PC}{B(N+1)}$$

When the formula is rearranged, to make N the subject, N is equal to:

A $\dfrac{2PC}{RB} - 1$

B $\dfrac{2PC - 1}{RB}$

C $2PC - 1$

D   None of these

31 The formula $\dfrac{1}{1.1}S^2 \div \left(1 - \dfrac{1}{1.1}\right)$ simplifies to:

A $\dfrac{S^2}{1.1}$

B S^2

C $\dfrac{10S^2}{1.1}$

D $10S^2$

32 In the equation C = 6 + 0.5Q, C denotes the total cost of sales (in thousands of $) and Q denotes the number of units sold (in thousands).

The total cost of sales for 3,000 units is therefore:

A $1,506.00

B $6,001.50

C $7,500.00

D $19,500.00

33 A $20,000 new car depreciates in value by 20% ± 2% each year (year-end). (The car depreciates by the 'reducing balance method', which means that a constant percentage is applied each year to the written down value.)

Therefore, after 3 years, the car's value is most accurately estimated by:

A between $9,491 and $11,027

B $10,240 ± $1,024

C $10,240 ± $205

D between $12,168 and $13,448

34 A trader's weekly costs, TC, are less than or equal to $100. Weekly revenue, R, is a minimum of $120.

Which ONE of the following statements is true?

A TC < $100 and R > $120 and R > TC

B TC ≥ $100 and R ≤ $120 and TC > R

C TC ≤ $100 and R > $120 and R < TC

D TC ≤ $100 and R ≥ $120 and R > TC

35 The following formula is used in the financial analysis of dividends:

$$R = \left(\frac{V}{P}\right) + G$$

When the formula is rearranged, with P in terms of the other variables, P is equal to:

A $\left(\dfrac{R}{V}\right) - G$

B $\dfrac{(R - G)}{V}$

C $\left(\dfrac{V}{R}\right) - G$

D $\dfrac{V}{(R - G)}$

36   The expression $(y^2)^3$ equals:

A $\sqrt[3]{y}$

B y^6

C y^5

D $y^{2/3}$

37   The term x^{-1} equals:

A $-x$

B $1/x$

C x^2

D $x - 1$

38   The price, p, of a product is planned to be £10, the planned annual demand, q, is 1,000 units and the number of trading days per year, n, is 200. If p, q and n are expected to vary by $\pm$ 10%, then the maximum value of $\frac{pq}{n}$, the mean revenue per trading day, will be closest to:

A   £37

B   £50

C   £55

D   £67

39   The expression $\left(x^3\right)^{-4}$ equals:

A $\sqrt[4]{x^3}$

B $\dfrac{1}{x^{12}}$

C $\sqrt[12]{x}$

D x^{-1}

40   The equations of two straight lines are given below:

$Y = 7 + X$ and $Y = 9 + 3X$

These lines intersect where the (X, Y) co-ordinates are equal to:

A   (-1,6)

B   (1,6)

C   (1,8)

D   None of these

41   If $aX^2 + bX + c = 0$, then $X = \dfrac{-b \pm \sqrt{(b^2 - 4ac)}}{2a}$

For $X^2 - 2X - 24 = 0$, then X equals:

A $\dfrac{-2 \pm 10}{2}$

B $\dfrac{-2 \pm \sqrt{92}}{2}$

C $\dfrac{2 \pm \sqrt{96}}{2}$

D $\dfrac{2 \pm 10}{2}$

42   A customer pays £228 for goods, having received a 5% discount. The undiscounted price was:

A   £240

B   £245

C   £250

D   £255

43   The series $X_1 + X_2 + X_3 + \ldots\ldots\ldots\ldots X_n$ can be expressed as:

A $3X$

B $\displaystyle\sum_{i=1}^{3} X_i + X_n$

C $\displaystyle\sum_{i=1}^{n} X_i$

D $3X + n$

44   The fraction x^{10}/x^6 equals:

A $\dfrac{4}{10x}$

B $6x^2$

C x^2

D x^4

45   XYZ Ltd purchase material for £40 per unit and seek to make a profit on the selling price of 20%. How much profit would they make if they sold 10 units per day?

A   £10

B   £20

C   £50

D   £100

46 In the following simultaneous equations if:

$3x + 4y = 25$ and

$5x + 3y = 27,$

the values of x and y are:

A   x=4, y=3

B   x=5, y=4

C   x=3, y=4

D   x=2, y=5

47 When $81^{-\frac{1}{n}} = 0.3333$, n is:

A   4

B   8

C   9

D   16

48 After 4 years of depreciation at 20% per year using the reducing balance method, the written down value of an asset was £9,625.60.

What was the original book value (to the nearest £)?

A   £19,960

B   £23,500

C   £29,530

D   £38,502

49 The price of an item at £24.99 including VAT at 17.5% is increased by 15%. The new price before VAT is added is (approximately):

A   £24.46

B   £28.74

C   £29.36

D   £33.77

50 The expression $(x^{\frac{1}{4}})^4$ equals:

A $x^{\frac{5}{4}}$

B x^4

C $x^{\frac{1}{16}}$

D x

51 A dress costs £36.78, including local sales tax of 18%, and is reduced in the sale by 20%. The new price before sales tax is £29.42 (to two decimal places).

True ☐

False ☐

52 The solution to the simultaneous equations $10x + 6y = 26$ and $6x - 2y = 24$ is:

x = ☐

y = ☐

53 There are 30 people in the workplace, 13 of whom have blond hair. What proportion of the staff (to 4 decimal places) do not have blond hair?

A   0.7666

B   0.7667

C   0.5666

D   0.5667

54 The equation of two straight lines are given below:

$y = 4 + x$

$x = 6 + 2y$

These lines intersect where the (x, y) co-ordinates are equal to:

x   ☐

y   ☐

55 If $y^2 = x^2 - 3x + 25$ and if $x = 3$, the value of y is:

☐

56 A retailer buys a box of light bulbs which nominally contains A units. The planned selling price of each unit is £B. If both A and B have been rounded to ± 10%, then the maximum rounding error in total revenue (to the nearest whole percent) is:

☐ %.

57 Veronica makes a number of visits each week. In a week where her average journey was 194 miles, her individual journey distances, in miles, were:

123, 268, x, 302, 99, 186, y

When $x = 4y$, the value of x is ☐

58 Mirjana and Sally share out a certain sum of money in the ratio 4:5 and Mirjana ends up with £7.

How much money was shared out?

£ ☐

How much money would have been shared out if Mirjana had got £7 and the ratio had been 5:4 instead of 4:5?

£ ☐

59   The sum of the squares of two numbers, x and y, is 769 and the difference between the
      numbers is 13. What do x and y equal?

      x = [   ] or [   ]

      y = [   ] or [   ]

60   A delicatessen sells bread flour for 50p per kg, or in bulk at £11 per 25 kg bag. The percentage
      saving (per kg) from buying a 25 kg bag is closest to:

      A   6.0%

      B   12.0%

      C   20.0%

      D   25.0%

61   When x = 5 the value (to two decimal places) of $(x^{0.25})^4$ = [   ]

62   The total cost of servicing 2 million transactions was estimated as £2 million. The volume
      estimate has an error of ± 0.5% and the cost estimate ± 5%. The minimum cost per transaction
      possible (to two decimal places) is £ [   ]

63   When x = 2, what is the value (to two decimal places) of the expression below?

      $\left(x^{-0.75}\right)^{-7}$

      A   Zero

      B   0.03

      C   38.05

      D   64.26

64   A square-ended rectangular box has a volume of 1,458 cm³. The length of the box is twice that
      of one side of the square end.

      One side of the square end therefore measures:

      A   6 cms

      B   9 cms

      C   18 cms

      D   24 cms

65   The expression $\dfrac{(x^2)^3}{x^5}$ equals:

      A   0

      B   1

      C   x

      D x^2

66   At a value added tax (VAT) rate of 12½%, an article sells for 84p including VAT. If the VAT rate increases to 17½%, the new selling price to the nearest penny will be:

   A   87p

   B   88p

   C   94p

   D   99p

67   In the formula $Q = \sqrt{\dfrac{2DC}{PR}}$, if Q = 100, C = 10, P = 6 and R = 0.2, then D, to the nearest unit, is:

   A   598

   B   599

   C   600

   D   601

68   An article in a sales catalogue is priced at £298 including value added tax (VAT) at 17.5%. The price, excluding VAT, to the nearest penny is:

   A   £247.34

   B   £253.62

   C   £255.00

   D   £280.50

69   The numeric value of the expression $\dfrac{(x^3)^3}{x^7}$ when x = 5 is:

   A   0

   B   5

   C   25

   D   125

70   An item priced at £90.68, including local sales tax at 19%, is reduced in a sale by 20%. The new price before sales tax is added is:

   A   £60.96

   B   £72.54

   C   £75.57

   D   £76.20

71   The expression $(x^8)^{-4}$ equals:

A $\sqrt[4]{x^8}$

B $\dfrac{1}{x^{32}}$

C $\sqrt[32]{x}$

D x^4

72   A coat which was priced at £45.99 last year is now £53.99. What is the percentage increase in price to two decimal places?

A   17.39%

B   17.40%

C   19.78%

D   20.09%

73   A radio which was priced at £56.99 has been reduced to £52.49. To two decimal places, the percentage reduction in price is:

A   7.89%

B   7.90%

C   8.57%

D   8.91%

74   The expression $(x^3)^4$ equals:

A x^7

B x^{12}

C $7x$

D $x/7$

75   A buyer has spent £30,151 on 550 units of a particular item. The first 100 units cost £50 each, the next 150 units cost £8,250 in total, the next batch cost £11,200 in total and the final 100 cost £x each. The value of x is:

A   £55.00

B   £56.00

C   £57.01

D   £60.30

76　A buyer purchases 20 cases of Product A at £7.84 per case, 10 cases of Product B at £8.20 per case, 12 cases of Product C at £8.50 per case and a number of cases of Product D at £8.60 per case. He spends £469.80 in total.

If there are 12 items in each case of Product D, how many ITEMS of Product D does he buy?

A　120

B　144

C　150

D　180

77　The expression $\left(x^{\frac{1}{8}} \right)^8$ equals:

A　$x^{\frac{9}{8}}$

B　x^8

C　$x^{\frac{1}{64}}$

D　x

78　Three years ago a retailer sold electronic calculators for £27.50 each. At the end of the first year he increased the price by 5% and at the end of the second year by a further 6%. At the end of the third year the selling price was £29.69 each. The percentage price change in year three was:

A　-3%

B　+3%

C　-6%

D　+9%

79　In a forecasting model based on y = a + bx, the intercept is 234. If the value of y is 491 and x is 20, then the value of the slope, to two decimal places, is:

A　-24.55

B　-12.85

C　12.85

D　24.85

80　The expression $\dfrac{a^{2x}}{a^{2y}}$ simplifies to:

A　$a^{2x/y}$

B　$a^{(x-y)/2}$

C　$a^{2(x-y)}$

D　$a^{2(x+y)}$

81   The formula $\dfrac{QH}{2} = \dfrac{DS}{Q}$ can be re-arranged so that Q equals:

A $\left(\dfrac{H}{2DS}\right)^2$

B $\sqrt{\dfrac{2DS}{H}}$

C $\sqrt{\dfrac{H}{2DS}}$

D $\left(\dfrac{2DS}{H}\right)^2$

82   The total profit, P, of an organisation is related to output (x units) by the expression:

P = 40 + 11x – 2x^2

The organisation will break even (that is, P = 0) with an output of:

A   2.5 units

B   4 units

C   5.5 units

D   8 units

83   The solution, in the form (x, y), to the simultaneous equations 3x + 2y = 6 and x – 2y = 2 is:

A   (0,3)

B   (2,3)

C   (2,0)

D   (3,2)

SUMMARISING AND ANALYSING DATA

84   An inflation index and index numbers of a company's sales (£) for the last year are given below.

Quarter:	1	2	3	4
Sales (£) index:	109	120	132	145
Inflation index:	100	110	121	133

'Real' sales, ie adjusted for inflation, are:

A   approximately constant and keeping up with inflation

B   growing steadily and not keeping up with inflation

C   growing steadily and keeping ahead of inflation

D   falling steadily and not keeping up with inflation

85   **A car travels 20 miles at 30 mph, then 10 miles at 60 mph.**

The mean speed for the whole journey of 30 miles is closest to (mph):

A   36

B   40

C   42

D   45

86   **When the mean purchase price of 10 units at 50p, 10 units at 70p, and 20 units at Xp is 80p, the value of X is:**

A   40p

B   60p

C   80p

D   100p

87   **In a histogram, one class is three quarters of the width of the remaining classes.**

If the score in that class is 21, the correct height to plot on the histogram is:

A   15.75

B   21

C   28

D   42

88   **The following scores are observed for the times taken to complete a task, in minutes:**

12, 34, 14, 15, 21, 24, 9, 17, 11 and 8

The median score is:

A   14.00

B   14.10

C   14.50

D   16.50

89   **Over a period a firm made purchases of £400, £500, £550 and £600 on items, the unit costs of which were £10.00, £12.50, £11.00 and £12.00 respectively.**

To the nearest penny, the average price paid per item was:

A   £11.21

B   £11.37

C   £11.39

D   £12.00

90 In a histogram, the common class width is £10.00. For analysis purposes, the analyst has set one class at £12.50 and the frequency recorded is 80 respondents. To maintain the accuracy of the histogram, the score which must be plotted is:

A   48

B   64

C   80

D   100

91 A group of people have the following ages:

21, 32, 19, 24, 31, 27, 17, 21, 26 and 42 years.

The median age of the group is:

A   21 years

B   25 years

C   26 years

D   31 years

92 In a negatively skewed distribution,

A   the mean is larger than the median

B   the mean is smaller than the median

C   the mean is the same as the median

D   the mean lies between the median and the mode

93 The following set of data:

13, 42, x, 7, 51, 69, 28, 33, 14, 8

has a median of 29. What is the value of x?

A   25

B   29

C   30

D   32

94 A firm represents the sales of its various products in a pie-diagram. The segment for the £250,000 sales of product X is represented on the pie-diagram by a segment of 10 degrees. Total sales for the firm are:

A   £2.5 million

B   £5 million

C   £7.5 million

D   £9 million

95   **A histogram uses a set of rectangles to represent a grouped frequency table. To be correctly presented, the histogram must show the relationship of the rectangles to the frequencies by reference to the:**

A   height of each rectangle

B   area of each rectangle

C   width of each rectangle

D   diagonal of each rectangle

96   **The essence of systematic sampling is that:**

A   each element of the population has an equal chance of being chosen

B   members of various strata are selected by the interviewers up to predetermined limits

C   every nth member of the population is selected

D   every element of one definable sub-section of the population is selected

97   **Eight people have the following individual weights, in kilograms:**

97   105   53   69   84   59   94   x

If the median weight is 78 kgs, then x is:

A   63 kgs

B   72 kgs

C   78 kgs

D   84 kgs

98   **A firm which bottles shampoo selects some filled bottles for examination. The procedure used is that two random numbers, x and y, are chosen. Starting at the xth bottle filled, every bottle at an interval of y is then chosen for examination.**

This type of sampling is known as:

A   Multi-stage

B   Random

C   Systematic

D   Stratified

99   **Secondary data is:**

A   data that does not provide any information

B   data collected for another purpose

C   data collected specifically for the purpose of the survey being undertaken

D   data collected by post or telephone, not by personal interview

100 Which of the following sampling methods does not require the sampling frame?

A   Random

B   Stratified

C   Quota

D   Systematic

101 The number of new orders received by five salesmen last week was: 2, 4, 6, 8, 10. The standard deviation of the number of new orders received is:

A   2.40

B   2.83

C   6.63

D   8.00

The following data is to be used for Questions 102 and 103.

The exam marks for nine students were:

55	86	37	56	72	55	64	70	45

---

102 The mode of the exam marks is:

A   55

B   56

C   60

D   86

103 The median of the exam marks is:

A   55

B   56

C   60

D   86

104 The coefficient of variation is used to measure:

A   the correlation between two variables

B   the percentage variation in one variable caused by variation in another

C   the strength of a relationship between two variables

D   relative dispersion

105 The following table shows that the typical salary of part qualified management accountants in five different regions of England.

Area	Typical salary £
South-east	21,500
Midlands	20,800
North-east	18,200
North-west	17,500
South-west	16,700

The best diagram to draw to highlight the differences between areas is:

A   a pie diagram

B   a multiple bar chart

C   a percentage component bar chart

D   a simple bar chart

106 The numbers of rejects from 50 samples of the same size is as follows:

Number of rejects in each sample:	0	1	2	3	4	5
Number of samples (frequency of rejects):	5	10	10	20	5	0

The arithmetic mean number of rejects per sample is:

A   2.2

B   2.4

C   3

D   20

107 On which ONE of the following graphics can the median readily be found without further calculation?

A   Bar chart

B   Cumulative frequency curve

C   Histogram

D   Pie chart

108 The following statements are often made about 'simple random sampling'.

(i)   It ensures a representative sample.

(ii)   It eliminates selection bias.

Which of the following is always true?

A   (i) only

B   (ii) only

C   Both (i) and (ii)

D   Neither (i) nor (ii)

109 An accountant has to check a sample of invoices. The invoices are divided into three groups, by value as follows: 'under £100', '£100 - £500' and 'over £500'. Samples are then selected randomly from each group.

Which ONE of the following sampling methods is involved?

A   Cluster

B   Multi-stage

C   Quota

D   Stratified

110 Details of an index number are given below:

Group	Base	Weight	Index
Food & Drink	100	50	140
Travel & Leisure	100	30	130
Housing	100	20	120
All items	100	100	??

The All items index number is closest to:

A   130

B   133

C   135

D   146

111 For the following set of ten numbers, the median is 15:

10   11   12   13   14   16   17   18   19   20+X

The statement is false if X equals:

A   -5

B   -4

C   -3

D   -2

112 An index number is made up of two items, food and non-food.

Sub-group	Weight	Index
Non-food	7	130
Food	3	?
All items	10	127

The index number for the sub-group Food is closest to:

A   120

B   122

C   124

D   126

113 A sample of 10% of CIMA students is required. Which ONE of the following methods will provide the best simple random sample?

    A   Select every tenth CIMA student to arrive at their college/institute on one specific day

    B   Select randomly, using random number tables, one in ten of every CIMA class

    C   Select 10% of colleges/institutions providing CIMA courses, then from these choose all students who are registered with CIMA

    D   Select 10% of all students registered with CIMA, giving each a chance of 0.1 of being picked

114 Sales for the first five months of the year averaged £8,200 per month.

For the last four months of the year sales averaged £8,500 per month.

If sales for the year totalled £102,000, the average for the sixth, seventh and eighth months must be:

    A   £8,500

    B   £9,000

    C   £9,500

    D   £10,200

115 In 1990, a price index based on 1980 = 100 had a value of x.

During 1990, it was re-based at 1990 = 100, and in 1998 the new index stood at 112.

If the total price movement between 1980 and 1998 was an increase of 40%, what was the value of x in 1990, ie before re-basing?

    A   125

    B   128

    C   136

    D   140

116 What is the value of the quartile deviation of the following set?

    31   68   38   42   43   40   60

    A   11

    B   22

    C   42

    D   46

117 In January 1995 the average pay for Grade B workers was £200 per week. There was a contract in force index-linking the pay for the next five years, with increases effective from 1 January each year, starting in 1996. Details of the relevant price index for the last four years are:

Index of prices each January (January 1990 = 100)

Year	1995	1996	1997	1998	1999
Price Index	125	131	136	140	144

The average weekly pay for Grade B workers during 1999 was (to the nearest pound):

A £206

B £230

C £250

D £280

118 The numbers of hours worked last week by a company's 11 employees were:

P	Q	R	S	T	U	V	W	X	Y	Z
35	36	36	36	40	38	40	37	35	42	43

The median number of hours worked last week was:

A 36

B 37

C 38

D 39

119 An index number increases each year by 10% of its value in the previous year. If its value in 1999 was 120, its value in 2002 is closest to:

A 150

B 156

C 160

D 162

120 Which ONE of the following describes a *qualitative* variable?

A The number of invoices selected for an internal audit

B The number of errors discovered in batches of invoices

C The £ value of the error made in invoices in a batch

D The type of error made in invoices

121 An accountant has marked some performance criteria out of 20 and found the mean to be 10 marks and the standard deviation to be 2 marks. The marks now have to be expressed as a percentage.

What would be the new value of the standard deviation?

A $\sqrt{10\%}$

B $\sqrt{20\%}$

C 10%

D 20%

122 Sample 1: 2, 5, 5, 12 and Sample 2: 1, 3, 5, 8, 8

Which of the following statistics has the same value in both samples?

A Arithmetic mean

B Standard deviation

C Median

D Mode

123 The number of daily complaints to a railway company has an average (arithmetic mean) of 12 and a standard deviation of 3 complaints.

The coefficient of variation, measured as a percentage, is therefore:

A 0.25%

B 4%

C 25%

D 400%

124 A driver makes a number of deliveries in a week. In a week where his average journey was 267 miles, his individual journey distances, in miles, were;

286, 192, x, 307, 185, y, 94

When $y = 4x$, the value of x is:

A 161

B 167

C 267

D 644

125 Each of the following diagrams shows a histogram of data with equal area. The vertical and horizontal scales of each histogram are identical.

Which set of data (histogram) has the largest standard deviation?

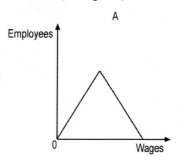

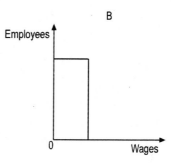

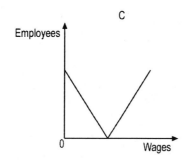

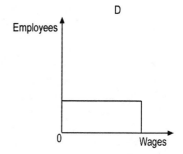

126 The quarterly sales (units) of a company are given in the table below.

Year	Q1	Q2	Q3	Q4
1997	13	52	56	79
1998	29	43	48	80
1999	24	55	46	75

Read the following statements:

(i)   Annual sales are static.

(ii)   The fourth quarter, Q4, has the highest quarterly sales in each of the three years.

(iii)   The mean sales for the second quarter (Q2) equals the mean quarterly sales for the whole period, 1997-99.

Which is true?

A   (i) only

B   (i) and (ii) only

C   (ii) and (iii) only

D   (i), (ii) and (iii)

127   The average prices of four commodities, along with the number of units used annually by a company, are given in the following table:

Commodity	Year 1 Price per unit £	Year 2 Price per unit £	Quantity Units
A	10	11	10
B	20	24	1
C	50	52	5
D	100	105	4

The price index for year 2 based on year 1, calculated using the weighted average of relatives method, is (to the nearest whole number):

A   106

B   107

C   108

D   110

128   The unit price of Brand X in May 2000 and May 2001 was as follows:

Year	2000	2001
Unit price of Brand X	£1.40	£1.75

The price relative for Brand X in May 2001, with base May 2000 = 100 is:

A   80

B   120

C   125

D   135

129   In a particular country, a tax at 40% is payable on any gains on house sales not due to inflation. A house was purchased there for $75,000 and sold for $250,000. Over the same period, the country's house price (inflation) index rose from 120 to 240.

The tax (to the nearest $) payable on the house sale is:

A $28,000

B $37,500

C $40,000

D $70,000

The next two questions, 130 and 131, are based on the following data.

	1998	1999	2000	2001
Weekly money wages index (1998 = 100)	100	105	110	115
Index of inflation (1990 = 100)	180	190	200	210

Read the following statements about the period 1998 to 2001:

(i)   Inflation has increased by more than money wages.

(ii)   Money wages have increased by 5% each year, year on year.

---

130   Which ONE of the following is true?

A   (i) only

B   (ii) only

C   Both (i) and (ii)

D   Neither (i) nor (ii)

131   'Real wages' are money wages that have been adjusted for inflation, ie 'deflated'. Over the period 1998 to 2001, real wages have (approximately):

A   remained unchanged

B   decreased by 1.43%

C   decreased by 1.67%

D   increased by 1.45%

132   The arithmetic mean of the following ten scores in a test is 20.

Y, 15, 22, 14, 21, 15, 20, 18, 27 and Y

What is the value of Y?

A   19

B   20

C   24

D   28

133   In a histogram, one class is ⅝ of the width of the other classes. If the score in that class is 400, the correct height to plot on the histogram is:

A   150

B   250

C   400

D   640

134   The price index for a commodity in the current year is 87 (base year =100) and the current price is £490 per unit.

What was the price in the base year?

A   £462.30

B   £553.70

C   £563.22

D   £577.00

135 In a period, a trader typically sells 100 garments. Because of random market conditions his buying-in price varies from £8 to £12 per garment and his selling price varies from £17 to £23 per garment. The buying and selling prices are independent. The range of his possible profit is:

A   £500

B   £700

C   £1,000

D   £1,500

136 The variable cost of a unit is established at £5 ± 10% and the selling price is £7 ± 15%. Estimated sales are 40,000 ± 20% units.

The range of total contribution possible is:

A   £76,000

B   £80,000

C   £142,000

D   £156,000

137 A firm divides its total costs into materials, wages and overheads, and deducts total costs from sales value to calculate profit. In a period when sales were £120 million, the firm made 12% profit margin on sales. Overheads were 4 times greater than wages and wages were twice as much as materials.

If sales value was represented on a pie chart with segments depicting the various costs and profit, the segment for overheads would be approximately how many degrees?

A   64

B   77

C   106

D   230

138 A histogram can also be called an ogive.

True ▢

False ▢

139 The following set of data has a median of 33. What is the value of x?

23, 14, 56, 78, 34, x, 5, 17, 70, 39

A   24

B   40

C   35

D   32

140 Consider the following set of data.

23, 45, 9, 53, 71, 26, 31, 14, 7, 16

The mean of the set of data is ▢ .

141   The mean height of 10 boxes is 120cm. If the individual heights in cm are 130, 160, 142, 91, 84, x, 176, 77, 100, 114 the value of x is [   ] cm.

142   The exam marks for 11 students were 49, 55, 67, 78, 56, 67, 89, 57, 51, 68, 82. The mode of the exam marks is [   ] .

143   The exam marks for 11 students were 55, 42, 67, 87, 55, 62, 78, 72, 52, 60, 59. The median of the exam marks is [   ] .

144   The number of new orders received by five area sales representatives last week was 4, 8, 12, 16, 20. The variance of the number of new orders received is [   ] .

145   The coefficient of variation is used to measure:

   A   relative dispersion

   B   correlation between two variables

   C   percentage variation in one variable caused by variation in another

   D   strength of the relationship between two variables

146   A histogram uses rectangles to represent a grouped frequency table. To be correctly presented, a histogram must show the relationship of rectangles to the frequencies by reference to the area. True or false?

   True [   ]
   False [   ]

147   A histogram has a standard interval width of 5 units. One interval has a width of 7.5 units. If the frequency of this interval is 15, the height of the corresponding bar is [   ] (to one decimal place).

148   In July 1996, the average pay for factory workers was £150 per week. There was a contract in force that index-linked the pay for the next five years, starting on 1 July 1997 and effective each year thereon. Details of the relevant price index for the last four years are as follows:

Index of prices each July (July 1991 = 100)

Year	1996	1997	1998	1999	2000
Price index	122	129	134	138	146

The average weekly pay for factory workers during 2000 (to the nearest £) was £ [   ] .

149   A small distribution company awards a 7% salary increase to every employee. Which of the following statements about the distribution of the company's salaries is/are correct?

   A   The standard deviation will stay the same

   B   The standard deviation will increase by 7%

   C   The coefficient of variation will remain unaltered

150   The price index for a product in the current year is 130 (base year = 100). The current price for the product is £175.

The price (to the nearest £) in the base year was therefore £ [   ] .

151 Primary data is data which has been expressly collected for a particular enquiry, for example, by observation or intervals. True or false?

True ☐

False ☐

152 The following tables shows the heights of a sample of 60 coffee tables:

Height of coffee table (cm)		Frequency
At least	less than	
10	20	5
20	30	12
30	40	15
40	50	17
50	60	7
60	70	4
		$\Sigma f = 60$

The arithmetic mean of this data is ☐ .

The value of the upper quartile in this frequency distribution (to the nearest cm) is ☐ .

153 In a large telephone company, the number of employees and the annual earnings per employee are shown as follows:

Annual earnings £	Number employed
20,000	6
30,000	6
60,000	10
70,000	2
80,000	4
110,000	3

The median value of annual earnings is £ ☐ .

154 The following table shows the values of orders made by customers in the last week:

Value of order (£)		Frequency
at least	less than	
1	10	5
10	20	7
20	30	11
30	40	16
40	50	10
50	60	4
60	70	3

The value of the lower quartile in this frequency distribution (to two decimal places) is ☐ .

155   **For the following set of 8 numbers, the median is 10.**

5, 6, 8, 9, 11, 13, 14, 17 + x

This is false if x equals:

A   -7

B   -6

C   -5

D   -4

156   **Which of the following can be classified as secondary data sources?**

A   *The Times*

B   A financial news website

C   A questionnaire

D   CIMA *Insider*

157   **Which of the following statements about 'simple random sampling' are always true?**

☐   It ensures the sample is representative.

☐   It eliminates selection bias.

158   **Which of these statements about the coefficient of variation is true?**

The coefficient of variation is a measure expressing:

A   the standard deviation as a percentage of the mean

B   the mean as a ratio of the standard deviation

C   the variation between the mean and the mode

D   the correlation between the values.

159   **In a histogram in which one class interval is three times as wide as the remaining classes, the height to be plotted in relation to the frequency for that class is ⬚.**

160   **The price index for a commodity in the current year is 150 (base year = 100). The current price for the commodity if £65.67 per kg.**

What was the price per kg (to two decimal places) in the base year? £ ⬚

161   **Nine packages were weighed in a factory. Their weights (in kg) are given below:**

33, 45, 39, 56, 44, 36, 50, 61, 56.

The mean of the weights (to two decimal places) is   ⬚

The median of the weights (to two decimal places) is   ⬚

The mode of the weights (to two decimal places) is   ⬚

162 **An ogive is:**

    A   another name for a histogram

    B   a chart showing any linear relationship

    C   a chart showing a non-linear relationship

    D   a graph of a cumulative frequency distribution

163 **When forecasting future costs, a manager puts a margin of 5% either side of each cost. If the upper estimate of a particular cost is stated as £21.50, then the mid-point of the estimate, to two decimal places, is:**

    A   £20.42

    B   £20.46

    C   £20.47

    D   £20.48

164 **In a normally distributed population with a mean score of 850 and a standard deviation of 74.63, the lower quartile score will be approximately:**

    A   700

    B   750

    C   800

    D   900

165 **The price index for a commodity in the current year is 135 (base year = 100). The current price for the commodity is £55.35 per kg.**

What was the price per kg in the base year?

    A   £35.00

    B   £41.00

    C   £74.72

    D   £100.00

166 **In 1994, a price index based on 1980 = 100 stood at 126. In that year it was re-based at 1994 = 100. By 1996, the new index stood at 109. For a continuous estimate of price changes since 1980, the new index may be expressed, to two decimal places, in terms of the old as:**

    A   85.51

    B   137.34

    C   135.00

    D   135.68

The following data should be used for Questions 167 and 168.

The numbers of houses sold by an estate agent in the last 8 weeks were:

4, 3, 2, 0, 0, 10, 1, 4

167 The median number of houses sold per week was:

A   0

B   2.5

C   3.0

D   5.0

168 The arithmetic mean number of houses sold per week was:

A   0

B   2.5

C   3.0

D   5.0

169 In order to carry out a survey into the spending habits of the population living in a certain region of the United Kingdom, a random sample of individuals is to be selected. The population can be categorised according to age group ('under 18', '18 to under 30', '30 to under 60', '60 and above'). The sample will consist of 0.5% of the membership of each age group. This method of sampling is an example of:

A   Stratified

B   Quota

C   Systematic

D   Random

PROBABILITY

170 In a group of 100 CIMA students, 30 are male, 55 are studying for Certificate Stage and 6 of the male students are not studying for Certificate Stage. A student chosen at random is female. What is the probability that she is not studying Certificate Stage?

A   0.80

B   0.56

C   0.44

D   0.20

171 A normal distribution has a mean of 55 and a variance of 14.44. The probability of a score of 59 or more is approximately:

A   0.15

B   0.35

C   0.50

D   0.65

172   In a student survey, 40% of the students are male and 80% are CIMA candidates. The probability that a student chosen at random is either female or a CIMA candidate is:

A   0.48

B   0.60

C   0.92

D   1.00

173   In a normally distributed population with a mean score of 850 and a standard deviation of 74.63, the lower quartile score will be approximately:

A   700

B   750

C   800

D   900

174   A sales representative visits two independent firms - A and B. The probability of making a sale at A is 0.3 and the probability of making a sale at B is also 0.3.

What is the probability of making no sale at all?

A   0.09

B   0.30

C   0.49

D   0.70

175   A sales representative makes calls to three separate unrelated customers. The chance of making a sale at any one of them is 60%. The probability that a sale is made on the third call only is:

A   0.096

B   0.216

C   0.36

D   0.4

176   A company has a normally distributed sales pattern for one of its products with a mean of £110. The probability of a sale worth more than £120 is 0.0119. Using CIMA Mathematical Tables, the standard deviation (to two decimal places) associated with sales is:

A   4.41

B   4.42

C   4.43

D   4.44

177 From past records it is known that 10% of items from a production line are defective. If two items are selected at random, what is the probability that only one is defective?

A   0.09

B   0.10

C   0.18

D   0.20

178 Because of the nature of the process, only two outputs are possible from a cell culture process. Probabilities of the outputs of cultures are as follows:

Number of cultures per day	Probability
25	0.4
35	0.6

Daily production is independent.

What is the probability that over a two-day period, the number of cultures will be 60?

A   0.24

B   0.36

C   0.48

D   1.00

179 In a normal distribution with a standard deviation of 30, 2.28% of the population is greater than 160.

The mean is:

A   30

B   60

C   90

D   100

180 In a survey of a housing estate, 30% of tenants had satellite television and 80% had video recorders. The probability that a household chosen at random had either a satellite television or a video recorder is:

A   0.24

B   0.30

C   0.80

D   0.86

181 A company is about to launch a new product. It has been predicted that, in each of the first two years, there are two possible levels of sales, high or low. The probability of sales being high in the first year is 0.3. If the first year's sales are high, the probability of high sales in the second year is 0.9. If sales are low in the first year, the probability of high sales in the second year is 0.2.

The probability of low sales in both years is:

A   0.8

B   0.56

C   0.90

D   1.5

182 The distribution of sales is normal, with a mean of 150 items per week, and variance of 100 items. The probability that sales are less than 170 items in any week is:

A   0.0793

B   0.4772

C   0.5793

D   0.9772

183 Three independent experts have estimated the probability of a company's future annual sales:

Sales	High [£1m]	Medium [£0.5m]	Low [£0.25m]
Expert W	0.2	0.3	0.5
Expert X	0.1	0.4	0.5
Expert Y	0.1	0.6	0.3

The highest expected value for the company's estimated annual sales is given by:

A   W only

B   X only

C   Y only

D   both W and Y.

184 Three people are carrying out independent functions during an internal audit. It is known that in each of the three separate areas being investigated there is a serious error. From past experience, it is estimated that the (independent) chances of the individuals finding the serious error in their area are 0.8, 0.7 and 0.6.

The probability that at *least one* of the serious errors will be found is:

A $(0.8 \times 0.3 \times 0.4) + (0.2 \times 0.7 \times 0.4) + (0.2 \times 0.3 \times 0.6)$

B $1 - (0.2 \times 0.3 \times 0.4)$

C $1 - (0.8 \times 0.7 \times 0.6)$

D   None of the above

185 **A garage has experienced the following regular weekly demand for its hire cars over the last 50 weeks:**

Weekly demand for hire cars: 0   1   2   3   4   5 or more

Number of weeks (frequency): 10   5   15   15   5   0

The expected value of weekly demand equals:

A   2.0 cars

B   2.2 cars

C   2.5 cars

D   None of these

186 **The lengths of a very large batch of metal rods are Normally distributed with a mean length of 300 millimetres and a standard deviation of 10 millimetres.**

The percentage of the batch which is longer than 285 millimetres is closest to:

A   43%

B   57%

C   84%

D   93%

The following data should be used for 187 and 188.

In an internal audit of 200 invoices, the following number of errors were discovered:

Number of errors	0	1	2	3	4	5	6 or more
Number of invoices	60	30	40	40	20	10	0

187 **The percentage of invoices with errors is:**

A   30%

B   70%

C   80%

D   None of these

188 **The expected value of the number of errors per invoice is:**

A   1.8

B   2

C   2.1

D   3

189 **The length of telephone calls to a Software Support line is approximately normally distributed with a mean of 20 minutes and a standard deviation of 5 minutes.**

The percentage of calls lasting under 30 minutes is closest to:

A   2%

B   48%

C   83%

D   98%

---

190 A company's security system is made up of three separate electronic alarms, which operate independently. The security system operates provided that at least one of the three alarms is working. The probability of an alarm failing at any time is 1 in 100.

The probability of the security system failing is:

A   1 in 100

B   3 in 100

C   1 in 10,000

D   1 in 1,000,000

191 The (possible) price increase of product X next week is denoted by X, and the (possible) price increase of product Y next week is denoted by Y. P denotes probability.

$P(X) = \frac{2}{5}$ $P(Y) = \frac{1}{5}$ $P(X/Y) = \frac{1}{2}$

Therefore P(Y/X) equals:

A $\frac{1}{4}$

B $\frac{3}{10}$

C $\frac{1}{2}$

D $\frac{3}{5}$

The following information is to be used for Questions 192 to 194.

A company selling sports clothes and equipment has analysed the expenditure habits of a random sample of 500 of its customers, and produced the following table showing the number of customers in each category:

Expenditure	Age of customer	
	Under 25	25 and over
Under £50	55	205
£50 to £200	125	80
Over £200	10	25

---

192 The probability that a customer is under 25 and spent between £50 and £200 is:

A   0.20

B   0.25

C   0.61

D   0.66

193 The probability that a customer aged under 25 spent between £50 and £200 is:

A   0.20

B   0.25

C   0.61

D   0.66

194 The probability that a customer who spent between £50 and £200 is aged under 25 is:

    A   0.20

    B   0.25

    C   0.61

    D   0.66

195 The lengths of steel rods are normally distributed with a mean of 100mm and a standard deviation of 5mm.

The percentage of steel rods with a length of less than 95mm is closest to:

    A   5%

    B   16%

    C   20%

    D   34%

196 The staff in the Complaints Department of an airline are available to answer the telephone at random times, which amount to 20% of the working day on average.

The probability that a customer's call is answered for the first time, on their fifth attempt is:

    A $(0.2)^5$

    B $(0.2)^4 \times (0.8)$

    C $(0.8)^4 \times (0.2)$

    D   1

The next four questions, 197 to 200, are based on the following table of data.

Mail order buyers of Brand X classified by area and age (years)

Age	Under 25	25–44	45–64	65 +
Area				
North	400	350	300	250
South	600	550	500	450
East	200	150	100	50
West	400	350	300	250
Totals	1,600	1,400	1,200	1,000

197 The probability that a randomly-selected Brand X buyer is from the North *and* under 25 years of age is (to 2 decimal places):

    A   0.08

    B   0.25

    C   0.31

    D   0.56

198 The probability that a randomly-selected Brand X buyer is from the West *or* under 25 years of age is (to 2 decimal places):

A   0.08

B   0.48

C   0.56

D   None of these

199 The probability that a randomly-selected Brand X buyer, *who is under 25 years of age*, is from the South is (to 3 decimal places):

A   0.115

B   0.286

C   0.375

D   None of these

200 The probability that two randomly-selected Brand X buyers are both under 25 years of age is (to two decimal places):

A   0.09

B   0.31

C   0.62

D   None of these

201 In a single throw of a pair of fair (six-sided) dice, what is the probability that the result is two numbers which sum to 7?

A $\frac{1}{12}$

B $\frac{1}{6}$

C $\frac{1}{4}$

D $\frac{1}{2}$

202 An item is made in two stages. At first it is processed by one of four machines – A, B, C, or D – with equal probability. At the second stage it is processed by one of two machines – E or F – and is twice as likely to go through F as this machine works twice as quickly.

The probability that an item is processed on A or E is:

A $\frac{1}{12}$

B $\frac{2}{7}$

C $\frac{1}{2}$

D $\frac{7}{12}$

203   A manufacturer supplies components in boxes of 10, stating that there is a (independent) 10% chance of any one component being faulty.

In a large batch, the percentage of boxes containing no faulty components will be closest to:

A   10%

B   35%

C   50%

D   90%

204   To win a prize at the fair you have to make the correct selection of colour of a ball which you have no control over. There are 100 balls in total, of which 10 are blue, 40 are red, 30 are green and 20 are brown. Only the blue ball wins a prize. What is the probability of selecting a loser?

A   0.9

B   0.7

C   0.5

D   0.2

205   City and United are great rivals. They play each other twice over a season. If the form book reckons that each side has an equal chance of winning both matches, what is the probability that City will do the double, ie beat United twice?

A   1 in 4

B   1 in 6

C   1 in 8

D   1 in 9

206   A normal distribution has a mean of 200 and a variance of 36. The lower quartile of this distribution is therefore (to the nearest whole number):

A   50

B   194

C   196

D   206

207   In a customer survey at a Garden Centre, 40% of customers are male and 70% spend £10 or more.

The probability that a customer chosen at random is either female or spends less than £10 is:

A   0.18

B   0.60

C   0.72

D   0.90

208   A normal distribution with a standard deviation of 40 units has a mean of 150 units.

What proportion of the population is below 175 units (to the nearest %)?

A   23%

B   27%

C   63%

D   74%

209   In a recent survey it was found that 35% of students at a college were male and 70% are studying law. The probability that a student chosen at random is either female or studying law is [   ] % (to two decimal places).

210   A company needs to decide between two projects - Project X and Project Y. The profits that may be generated from each project are as follows:

Project X		Project Y	
Probability	Profit	Probability	Profit
0.4	£3,000	0.35	£10,000
0.6	£1,500	0.65	£0

Which project should be chosen? [   ]

What is the associated expected value of profit? [   ]

211   A normal distribution has a mean of 100 and a standard deviation of 20. Approximately 80% of the population is below which of the following values?

A   139

B   220

C   117

D   126

212   Four coins are tossed. The probability (to two decimal places) of getting exactly four heads is [   ] .

213   The lengths of fence panels are normally distributed, with a mean length of 200cm and a standard deviation of 5cm. The percentage of fence panels with a length of less than 190cm is [   ] % (to two decimal places).

214   Which of the following are properties of the normal distribution?

A   It is symmetrical and bell shaped

B   The area under the curve is one unit of area

C   The mean, median and mode lie together in the axis of the symmetry of the curve

215   In a factory, it is known that 12% of light bulbs are defective. If two are chosen at random, what is the probability (to two decimal places) that only one is defective? [   ]

216   A book seller visits two independent households – A and B. The probability of making a sale at A is 0.25 and the probability of making a sale at B is 0.5. The probability of making no sale at all is therefore [   ] (to two decimal places).

217   If the distribution of sales of yoghurts is normal, with a mean of 110 yoghurts per week and a variance of 50 yoghurts, the probability that sales are less than 130 in any week is [   ] (to four decimal places).

218   In a magazine survey it was found that 60% of readers were female and 25% had blue eyes. The probability that a reader chosen at random is either male or has blue eyes is [   ] (to two decimal places).

219   A specialist record shop has analysed the spending habits of a random sample of 250 of its customers and produced the following table showing the number of customers in each category.

| | Age of customers | | |
Expenditure	Under 18	18 or older	Total
Under £20	20	65	85
£20 – £40	60	40	100
Over £40	30	35	65
Total	110	140	250

The probability that a customer is aged under 18 and spent between £20 and £40 is [   ] (to two decimal places).

If a customer is aged under 18, the probability that he spent between £20 and £40 is [   ] (to two decimal places).

220   In a very large university, 60% of the students are women and 15% of all students are studying economics. There is no correlation between gender and subject. If two students are chosen at random, the probability, as a percentage, that each of them is a woman or studying economics is [   ] (to two decimal places).

221   If one card is drawn from a standard pack of 52 playing cards, what is the probability of getting a spade or a king (to two decimal places)?

Probability

King   Spade   King of Spades   King or Spade
[   ]   [   ]   [   ]   [   ]

222 Consider the following normal distribution:

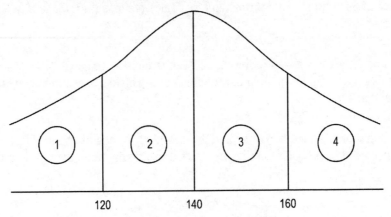

Identify which areas represent the following probabilities:

Probability X > 120 = ☐

Probability X < 120 = ☐

Probability X < 160 = ☐

223 The weights of balls are normally distributed, with a mean of 75kg and a standard deviation of 10kg. The percentage of balls above 84kg is ☐ % (to two decimal places).

224 In a survey of outpatients at a General Hospital, 40% are female and 70% are employed. The probability that an outpatient chosen at random is either male or employed is:

A   0.42

B   0.60

C   0.70

D   0.88

225 A sample of 100 companies has been analysed by size and whether they pay invoices promptly. The sample has been cross-tabulated into LARGE/SMALL against FAST PAYERS/SLOW PAYERS. 60 of the companies are classified as LARGE, of which 40 are SLOW PAYERS. In total, 30 of all the companies are FAST PAYERS.

The probability that a company chosen at random is a FAST PAYING SMALL COMPANY is:

A   0.10

B   0.20

C   0.30

D   0.40

226 With a standard deviation of 16.2, the upper value of a 99% confidence interval is 95.8. What is the value (to the nearest whole number) of the mean?

A   42

B   54

C   64

D   80

227   The following information shows the daily sales revenue (£000) of a company producing a particular item of clothing, over a period of two years:

Sales £000	Frequency %
0 to under 10	5
10 to under 20	20
20 to under 30	60
30 to under 40	10
40 to under 50	5

The expected daily **sales** (in £000) is:

A   22

B   24

C   26

D   None of these

The following data should be used for Questions 228 to 230.

The total overtime cost of a small company varies from week to week, and is found to be normally distributed with a mean of £800 and a standard deviation of £200.

---

228   In any given week, the probability that the overtime cost will exceed £1,000 is:

A   0.1587

B   0.3413

C   0.8413

D   None of these

229   In any given week, the probability that the overtime cost will be between £700 and £900 is:

A   0.3035

B   0.6170

C   0.3830

D   None of these

230   In 10% of weeks, the overtime cost will approximately fall below:

A   £366

B   £455

C   £544

D   £633

The following data should be used for Questions 231 to 234.

Two components, A and B, operate independently as part of a computer system. The probabilities that A and B will work correctly are 0.9 and 0.8 respectively.

231   The probability that both components will work correctly is:

   A   0.81

   B   0.72

   C   0.28

   D   0.17

232   The probability that both components will not work correctly is:

   A   0.02

   B   0.03

   C   0.3

   D   None of these

233   The probability that only one component will work correctly is:

   A   0.98

   B   0.81

   C   0.74

   D   0.26

234   The probability that at least one component will work correctly is:

   A   0.64

   B   0.81

   C   0.98

   D   None of these

FINANCIAL MATHEMATICS

235   If a single sum of £12,000 is invested at 8% per annum with interest compounded quarterly, the amount to which the principal will have grown by the end of year three is approximately:

   A   £15,117

   B   £14,880

   C   £15,219

   D   £15,880

236 A farmer is to lease a field for six years at an annual rent of £500, the rentals being paid at the beginning of each year.

What is the present value of the lease at 7%?

A   1,900

B   2,000

C   2,383

D   2,550

237 It is estimated that a particular cost will decline by 5% per annum on a compound basis. If the cost now is £10,000, by the end of year 4 the cost will be approximately:

A   £7,500

B   £8,000

C   £8,145

D   £8,500

238 The present value of a five-year annuity receivable which begins in one year's time at 5% per annum compound is £60,000. The annual amount of the annuity, to the nearest £, is:

A   £12,000

B   £13,860

C   £259,769

D   £300,000

239 It is estimated that, because of productivity improvements, costs will fall by 2½% per annum on a compound basis. If annual costs are now £160,000 then by the end of five years they will have fallen, to the nearest £, to:

A   £137,450

B   £140,000

C   £140,975

D   £145,590

240 The annual rent of a building is £1,200 payable in advance at the beginning of each year. At an interest rate of 14%, the present value of the rental payments is £5,319.60.

The length of the lease is:

A   3 years

B   4 years

C   5 years

D   6 years

241 A building society adds interest monthly to investors' accounts even though interest rates are expressed in annual terms. The current rate of interest is 6% per annum.

An investor deposits £1,000 on 1 January. How much interest will have been earned by 30 June?

A   £30.00

B   £30.38

C   £60.00

D   £61.68

242 An annuity of £x is to be received at the end of each of the next 7 years. If the present value of the annuity is £33,995.18 at 8%, then £x is:

A   £2,719.16

B   £4,856.45

C   £5,693.38

D   £6,530.00

243 An investor is to receive an annuity of £1,360 for six years commencing at the end of year 1. It has a present value of £6,101. What is the rate of interest?

A   6%

B   9%

C   12%

D   15%

244 A leasing agreement is for five years. £10,000 must be paid at the beginning of the first year, to be followed by four equal payments at the beginning of years two, three, four and five. At a discount rate of 8%, the present value of the four equal payments is £26,496. The total amount to be paid during the lease period is:

A   £32,000

B   £40,000

C   £42,000

D   £44,000

245 The difference between the total present value of a stream of cash flows at a given rate of discount, and the initial capital outlay is known as the:

A   internal rate of return

B   rate of return

C   net present value

D   net profit

246   A person is to receive a ten-year annuity of £5,000 per year, received at the end of each year. At what interest rate does this have a present value of £33,550?

A   2%

B   4%

C   8%

D   16%

247   An investor has funds to invest now to produce an annuity of £1,494.87 per year for ten years commencing in one year.

If prevailing interest rates are 7%, what is the maximum amount (to the nearest £) that should be invested?

A   £1,046

B   £10,500

C   £12,843

D   £14,949

248   A financial adviser leases an office for 5 years, the rentals being paid at the beginning of each year. At 10% the present value of the rentals is £32,800. To the nearest £, the annual rental is:

A   £3,280

B   £6,560

C   £7,866

D   £8,000

249   How much should be invested now (to the nearest £) to receive £8,000 per annum in perpetuity if the annual rate of interest is 7 per cent?

A   £560

B   £8,560

C   £72,864

D   £114,286

250   A company is considering purchasing a new machine for £25,000. This would increase the annual cash flow of the company by £6,500 in each of the next six years. If the cost of capital is 9 per cent per annum, the net present value of this investment is:

A   £4,159

B   £10,780

C   £10,901

D   £14,000

251 The net present value of an investment at 10 per cent is £12,000, and 18 per cent is -£4,000. The internal rate of return of this investment is:

A   12 per cent

B   14 per cent

C   16 per cent

D   22 per cent

252 An annual year-end income of £15,000 is required in perpetuity. Assuming a fixed rate of interest of 9% each year, and ignoring administrative charges, the sum required now to purchase the annuity is closest to:

A   £13,650

B   £135,000

C   £150,000

D   £167,000

253 A fixed-interest £200,000 mortgage, with annual interest compounded at 6% each year, is to be repaid by 15 equal year-end repayments of £R.

The annual repayment £R will be closest to:

A   £14,133

B   £20,593

C   £31,954

D   £83,400

254 You borrow £3,000 and pay 10% each year interest. Ignoring capital, if you pay this interest at the end of each year, what is the present value of the interest payable at the end of the third year?

A $\left(\frac{3}{10}\right) \times £300 \times 3$

B $\left(\frac{7}{10}\right) \times £300$

C $\left(\frac{10}{11}\right)^3 \times £300$

D $\left(\frac{11}{10}\right)^3 \times £400$

255 A firm has arranged a ten-year lease, at an annual rent of £8,000. The first rental payment has to be paid immediately, and the others are to be paid at the end of each year.

What (approximately) is the present value of the lease at 12%?

A   £50,640

B   £51,562

C   £45,200

D   £49,852

256   The sales of a product increase at a rate of 1% each month, month on month, for a year. This is equivalent to an annual percentage rate of expansion closest to:

A   11.3%

B   12.0%

C   12.7%

D   13.0%

257   An annual (year-end) income of £10,000 is required in perpetuity. If there is a fixed interest rate of 8% each year and administrative charges are ignored, the lump sum investment necessary now is closest to:

A   £9,260

B   £80,000

C   £100,000

D   £125,000

258   An investor is to receive an annuity of £8,000 for 10 years commencing in four years' time. At an 8% discount rate, the present value of the annuity is (approximately)

A   £6,400

B   £20,616

C   £42,622

D   £53,680

259   It is estimated that a particular cost will decline at the rate of 8% per annum on a compound basis.

If the cost is now £80,000, by the end of year 6 the cost will be (approximately):

A   £41,600

B   £48,508

C   £50,414

D   £52,000

260   At 10%, the present value of a ten-year annuity of £1,000 per annum commencing in 4 years is (approximately):

A   £4,615

B   £6,145

C   £9,000

D   £10,000

261 If £100 is invested for 3 years at an annual rate of interest of 10%, at the end of 3 years the investment should be worth:

A   £130

B   £132

C   £133

D   £133.10

262 How much would you need to invest now (to the closest £) if you wish to receive £30,000 per annum in perpetuity and the annual rate of interest is 6%? [   ]

263 An asset originally cost £500,000. It depreciates at 12% per year. Its value after six years is, therefore, £232,202 (to the nearest £).

True ☐

False ☐

264 A perpetuity is an annuity which lasts 10 years.

True ☐

False ☐

265 Matthew will receive a ten year annuity of £X per year, at the end of each year. At an interest rate of 6%, this annuity has a present value of £42,000.

The value of £X (to the nearest £) is £ [   ].

The following data should be used for Questions 266 and 267.

The following table shows the index of prices (1995 = 100) for a certain commodity over the period 1995 – 2000:

1995	1996	1997	1998	1999	2000
100	105	115	127	140	152

---

266 The percentage increase in the price between 1997 and 1999 is nearest to:

A   25.0

B   22.3

C   21.7

D   None of these

267 It has been decided to rebase the index so that 1998 = 100. The index for 2000 will now be nearest to:

A   193.1

B   139.4

C   125.0

D   119.7

The following data should be used for Questions 268 and 269.

£2,000 is invested in a bank account. The account earns compound interest at 5% per year.

268 The cash value of the account, to the nearest £, at the end of five years will be:

    A   £2,680

    B   £2,553

    C   £2,431

    D   £2,335

269 The investment will have almost doubled in value after:

    A   11 years

    B   12 years

    C   13 years

    D   14 years

270 An individual who expects to retire in five years' time estimates that his company pension will be £15,000 per year. Each year's pension will be paid as a lump sum at the end of the year. If current interest rates are 6%, then the present value of the first year's pension, to the nearest £5, will be:

    A   £10,575

    B   £10,975

    C   £11,190

    D   £11,205

271 A credit card company states that its nominal annual interest rate is 18%. If interest is charged monthly at 15%, then the annual percentage rate (APR), correct to two decimal places, will be:

    A   19.56%

    B   19.25%

    C   18.81%

    D   None of these

FORECASTING

272   If $\Sigma x = 440$, $\Sigma y = 330$, $\Sigma x^2 = 17,986$, $\Sigma y^2 = 10,366$, $\Sigma xy = 13,467$ and n = 11, then the value of r, the co-efficient of correlation, to two decimal places, is:

    A   0.98

    B   0.63

    C   0.96

    D   0.59

273   Based on 20 past quarters, the underlying trend equation for forecasting is y = 23.87 + 2.4x. If quarter 21 has a seasonal factor of times 1.08, using a multiplicative model, then the forecast for the quarter, in whole units, is:

    A   75

    B   80

    C   83

    D   85

274   Unemployment numbers actually recorded in a town for the second quarter of 20X7 were 2,200. The underlying trend at this point was 2,000 people and the seasonal factor is 0.97. using the multiplicative model for seasonal adjustment, the seasonally-adjusted figure (in whole numbers) for the quarter is:

    A   1,940

    B   2,061

    C   2,134

    D   2,268

275   Monthly sales have been found to follow a linear trend of y = 9.72 + 5.816x, where y is the number of items sold and x is the number of the month. Monthly deviations from the trend have been calculated and follow an additive model. In month 23, the trend value is estimated to be plus 6.5.

The forecast number of items to be sold in month 23 is approximately:

    A   130

    B   137

    C   143

    D   150

276 A forecasting model is based on the formula y = a + bx. Diagrammatically, this could be depicted as:

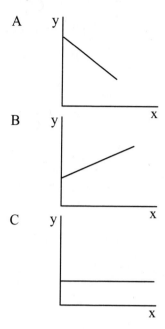

A   y

B   y

C   y

D   Either A or B or C depending on the value of b.

The following information is to be used for Questions 277 and 278.

In a time series analysis, the multiplicative model is used to forecast sales and the following seasonal variations apply:

Quarter	1	2	3	4
Seasonal variation	1.2	1.3	0.4	

The actual sales values for the first two quarters of 1999 were:

Quarter 1	£125,000
Quarter 2	£130,000

---

277 The seasonal variation for the fourth quarter is:

A   −2.9

B   0.9

C   1.0

D   1.1

278 The trend line for sales:

A   decreased between quarter 1 and quarter 2

B   increased between quarter 1 and quarter 2

C   remained constant between quarter 1 and quarter 2

D   cannot be determined from the information given

279   Which of the following could have a value of –2?

(i)   Correlation coefficient

(ii)   Slope of a regression line

(iii)   Variance

A   (ii) only

B   (i) and (ii) only

C   (i) and (iii) only

D   (ii) and (iii) only

280   The rank correlation coefficient between the ages and the scrap values of a certain type of machine equals –1.

This value means that:

A   no correlation exists between the ages and the scrap values of these machines

B   perfect correlation exists

C   weak negative correlation exists

D   a calculation error has been made

281   When forecasting future costs, a manager puts a margin of 5% either side of each cost. If the upper estimate of a particular cost is stated as £21.50, then the mid-point of the estimate, to two decimal places, is:

A   £20.42

B   £20.46

C   £20.47

D   £20.48

282   In a market research survey of a new drink, respondents were asked to rank eight drinks in order of preference regarding taste, and then rank them again for looks, with a rank of 1 indicating nicest taste and best looks. The rank correlation coefficient was calculated and was 0.95. This means that:

A   there appeared to be no correlation between taste and looks

B   the nicest drinks looked the best

C   the best-looking drinks did not taste very nice

D   nothing at all, as the rank correlation cannot be used for this kind of test

283   The calculation of a rank correlation coefficient [formula given in the *Mathematical Tables and Formulae*] shows that ten pairs of data are found to be perfectly negatively correlated.

Therefore, the value of $\sum d^2$ equals:

A   Zero

B   165

C   330

D   None of these

The following information is to be used for Questions 284 and 285.

A scatter diagram shows the weekly total costs of production (£) in a certain factory plotted against the weekly output (units). A broadly linear pattern is evident, with $r = 0.9$. The regression equation is:

Costs $= 1,500 + (15 \times \text{output})$.

Fifty data points have been included in the analysis, with output ranging from 100 units to 1,000 units. Output next week is planned to be 500 units.

284 **Read the following statements about estimates:**

(i)   Weekly fixed costs are approximately £1,500.

(ii)   Variable costs are approximately £15 per unit on average.

(iii) Next week's production costs are likely to be about £9,000.

Which one of the following is true, all other things being equal?

A   (i) and (ii) only

B   (i) and (iii) only

C   (ii) and (iii) only

D   (i), (ii) and (iii)

285 **Read the following statements:**

(i)   There is very little correlation between weekly costs of production and production level.

(ii)   90% of the variation in weekly costs is attributable to the amount produced.

(iii) Given the information, any forecast using the regression equation is likely to be very unreliable.

Which of the following is justified?

A   (ii) only

B   (i) and (iii) only

C   (ii) and (iii) only

D   None of them

The next two Questions, 286 and 287, are based on the following data.

A multiplicative time series model should be assumed.

Quarterly sales (units) of Brand X 2001

	Q_1	Q_2	Q_3
Sales (units)	1,600	4,400	1,680
Seasonal variation	-20%	+100%	-30%

286 **The trend value for Q_1 sales (units) is:**

A   1,280

B   1,920

C   2,000

D   None of these

287 The seasonal variation for Q_4 in 2001 is:

A   -50%

B   0%

C   +50%

D   None of these

288 For a certain group of students, the coefficient of rank correlation between their performance in Accounting and their performance in Law is –1. The coefficient of rank correlation between their performances in Law and FBSM is also –1. Therefore, the coefficient of rank correlation between their performance in Accounting and their performance in FBSM is:

A   –2

B   Zero

C   +1

D   Impossible to determine from the information given.

289

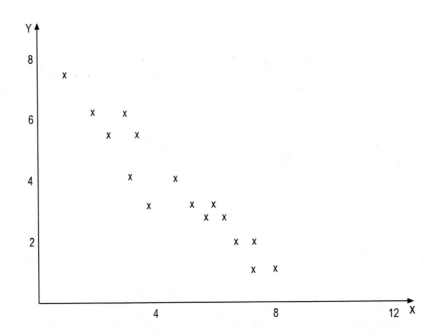

On the basis of the scatter diagram above, which of the following equations would best represent the regression line of Y on X?

A $Y = -X + 8$

B $Y = X + 8$

C $Y = X - 8$

D $Y = -X - 8$

290 **Based on the last twelve periods, the underlying trend of enquiries is y = 483.45 – 1.65x where y = number of enquiries and x = period number.**

If the 13th period has a seasonal factor of +21.45, assuming an additive forecasting model, then the forecast for period 13 (in whole units) is:

A   462

B   483

C   503

D   505

291 **The coefficient of determination (r^2) is a measure of how much the variation in the independent variable can be explained by variation in the dependent variable.**

True ☐

False ☐

292 **For a set of 12 racing cars, the following data has been found for the power in kw (x) and the top speed in mph (y).**

$\Sigma x = 802$

$\Sigma y = 1{,}850$

$\Sigma xy = 124{,}258$

$\Sigma x^2 = 53{,}792$

$\Sigma y^2 = 287{,}868$

The correlation coefficient to two decimal places is ☐ .

293 **Spurious correlation is where:**

A   two variables show a high degree of correlation as they are directly connected

B   two variables show a high degree of correlation but have no direct correlation

C   two variables show no correlation

294 **The regression equation linking x and y is y = 3x - 12. Which of the following is correct?**

A   the slope of the equation if plotted on a graph is -12

B   the slope of the equation if plotted on a graph is 3

C   the line cuts the x axis at 4 if plotted on a graph

D   the line cuts the x axis at -12 if plotted on a graph

295 **What is the equation of least squares regression line of y on x for the following four data pairs?**

x	y
2	6
3	8
4	12
5	12

y = ☐

296 The coefficient of determination, r^2, always falls within the range 0 to 1.

True ☐

False ☐

297 Which of the following statements are true?

A   The closer r is to +1 (or −1), the higher the degree of linear correlation

B   Rank correlation (R) is used when the values for x and y are non numeric

C   Correlation is a measure of how strong the connection is between the two variables

298 The bottom line of a Z chart depicting time series data shows:

A   the accumulated time series values

B   the actual times series values

C   the percentage increase in values

D   the moving total of values

299 In a time series analysis, the trend equation for a particular product is given by:

Trend $= 0.0004*YEAR^2 + 0.2*YEAR + 80.2$

Due to the cyclical factor, the forecast for 1996 is estimated at 1.87 times trend. In whole units, the forecast for 1996 is:

A   3,877

B   3,878

C   3,900

D   3,910

300 The following time series represents the weekly sales (£000) of a particular product:

Week	Sales £000
1	200
2	240
3	250
4	220
5	230
6	260

The second 4-point centred moving average for the sales data will be:

A   235.5

B   237.5

C   239.5

D   None of these

301 The estimated total cost of each unit of a product is £12 (± £1), and the estimated selling price of each unit is £20 (± £3). The estimated profit per unit will be:

   A   £8 (± £4)

   B   £8 (± £3)

   C   £8 (± £2)

   D   £8 (± £1)

302 For a set of six pairs of observations for the variables x (number of employees in hundreds) and y (product sales in thousands of units), the following results were obtained:

Σx = 1

Σy = 15

Σx^2 = 15

Σy^2 = 65

Σxy = 7

The correlation coefficient is nearest to:

   A   0.22

   B   0.47

   C   0.90

   D   -0.32

Section 2

PRACTICE QUESTIONS

BASIC MATHEMATICS

1   ENGINEERING ASSETS

The accounts of an engineering company contain data on the value of its assets over the last five years as follows:

Asset	20X1 £000	20X2 £000	20X3 £000	20X4 £000	20X5 £000
Property	59	59	65	70	74
Plant and machinery	176	179	195	210	200
Stock and work in progress	409	409	448	516	479
Debtors	330	313	384	374	479
Cash	7	60	29	74	74

Required:

(a)   Complete the following component bar chart and percentage component bar chart.

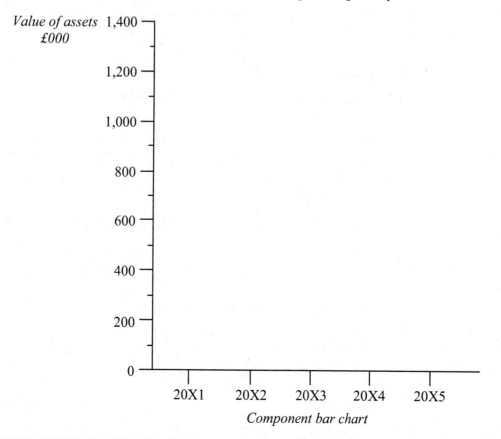

Component bar chart

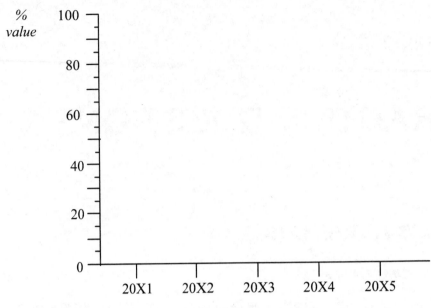

Percentage component bar chart

(8 marks)

(b) The total value of assets in 20X1 is £

The total value of assets in 20X5 is £

The percentage increase in the total value of assets over the five year period is:

% **(6 marks)**

(Total: 14 marks)

2   PROPORTIONAL REPRESENTATION

(a) A hostel charges £15 per night in the winter and £25.50 in the summer. The ratio of winter to summer prices is: **(1 mark)**

(b) A woman earns £6,000 per year and spends £4,500 per year. The ratio of her savings to her gross earnings is: **(2 marks)**

(c) The tax on a gross income of £8,700 is £1,450. The ratio of tax to gross income is: **(1 mark)**

(d) Two cars cost £4,500 and £5,500. After one year they are worth £3,250 and £4,000 respectively. The ratios of their prices (i) when new and (ii) secondhand are (answers correct to two decimal places): (i)   (ii)

(2 marks)

(e) An electronic printing calculator cost £95. A mini-computer with printer costs £1,425. The ratio of their prices is: **(1 mark)**

(f) The ratio of the commissions of two business representatives, one of whom receives £7,950 and the other £6,916.50 is: **(1 mark)**

(g) A batch of coins is made up of 32 kg of copper and 256 kg of nickel. The ratio of copper to nickel in the coinage alloy is: **(1 mark)**

(h) A bankrupt owes £28,900 and his goods, when sold, fetch £3,400. The ratio of cash available to debts payable is: **(1 mark)**

(Total: 10 marks)

3   SCHOOL COSTS

(a)   A school bursar estimates that the cost of text books for the following term will be £10 to the nearest £.

    (i)   The maximum absolute error in the cost is

    (ii)   The maximum relative error in the cost is

    (iii)   Explain the meaning of each type of error by completing the following sentences:

The maximum absolute error is ......

Your answer must not exceed 25 words.

The maximum relative error is ......

Your answer must not exceed 25 words.

(6 marks)

(b)   The bursar has also received estimates on the following items:

School uniform   £50 but could rise or fall by 5% over next year

School bus   £20 but could rise or fall by 4% over next year

School dance   £15 but could rise or fall by 3% over next year

    (i)   The maximum and minimum costs of each item are:

	Maximum	Minimum
School uniform		
School bus		
School dance		

    (ii)   The absolute maximum and minimum total expenditure on uniforms, bus and dance is:

	Maximum	Minimum

(9 marks)

(Total: 15 marks)

4   CALENDARS

A company specialises in the production of calendars. The total cost is made up of three elements: materials, labour and distribution.

Materials   50p per unit
Labour   £10 per hour
Distribution   £50 per hundred + £25

The set-up time for printing is two hours and calendars can be run off at a rate of 250 per hour.

(a)   The cost of producing 500 calendars is   **(6 marks)**

(b)   Produce a formula for the total cost £L in terms of N where N is the number of calendars produced. The formula is   **(8 marks)**

(c)   How many calendars can be produced for £1,000?

calendars   **(6 marks)**

(Total: 20 marks)

5   SIMULTANEOUS LINEAR EQUATIONS

(a)   Solve the following equations:

$$3x + 4y = 29$$
$$5x + 2y = 25$$

x =   y =

(4 marks)

(b) $$6x + 7y = 33$$
$$7x + 6y = 32$$

x =   y =

(4 marks)

(c) $$3x - 9y = 0$$
$$4x - 10y = 8$$

x =   y =

(4 marks)

(d) $$10x - 4y = 42$$
$$6x + 2y = 34$$

x =   y =

(4 marks)

(e) $$x + 2y = 0$$
$$4x - 2y = 50$$

x =   y =

(4 marks)

(Total: 20 marks)

SUMMARISING AND ANALYSING DATA

6 TYPES OF DATA

Complete the gaps in the following notes on:

(a) Raw data **(5 marks)**

(b) Secondary data **(3 marks)**

(c) Discrete and continuous data **(7 marks)**

(Total: 15 marks)

(a) RAW DATA is the set of _____ generated by a time series study, or by a cross-sectional study or by survey methods. The epithet raw is applied to the data in its state before it has been subjected to _____ Such data may merely be in the form of a list of cases which may have emerged in chronological order and in this form have no obvious meaning. The task of the statistician is to _____ the data in a more meaningful form by, for example, ordering it from highest value to lowest, by computing a measure of _____ such as the arithmetic mean and by calculating a measure of dispersion such as the _____ . In this way, we may examine the distribution of values and perhaps be able to compare one distribution with another to see if they exhibit any statistically significant differences.

(b) SECONDARY DATA is data that has not been collected by the user specifically _____ . It should be contrasted with primary data. Primary data is data that has been collected by the user specifically for _____ . When using secondary data, the user must be aware of the method of collection and the use for which the data was originally collected. To ignore such things as the sampling method or, for example, the type of questionnaire used to collect the original data could result in the secondary user using data that is _____ in some way.

(c) DISCRETE and CONTINUOUS DATA. There are two important types of variable quantity from the statistical viewpoint: those which vary discretely and those which vary continuously. A discrete variable is one which can take only a _____ number of _____ values (eg examination marks ranging from 1 to 100). On the other hand, time is a continuous variable. Graphically, discrete variables are usually represented by a series of _____ , whilst a continuous variable is represented by a _____ . In practice, discrete variables are often treated as continuous. A variable which can theoretically assume any value between two given values is a _____ variable, otherwise it is a _____ variable. If a variable can assume only one value, it is called a _____ .

7 PIGLET

Twenty products are sold by Piglet Limited. The annual sales by product over the last year were as follows.

Product	£000	Product	£000
1	16.4	11	91.8
2	112.6	12	19.4
3	59.4	13	34.2
4	29.2	14	73.8
5	104.6	15	30.6
6	110.0	16	58.4
7	92.2	17	78.4
8	62.6	18	45.4
9	75.2	19	64.2
10	56.4	20	96.0

Required:

(a) Prepare the following cumulative percentage table of total annual sales value that groups of products represent (grouping products together using intervals of £20k).

	1	*2*	*3*	*4*
	Products	*Frequency*	*Cumulative frequency*	*Cumulative percentage*
£0 to				
to				
to				
to				
to				
to				

(*Note:* It is not necessary to put the product numbers in the table. This has been included for tutorial purposes only.) **(10 marks)**

(b) Sketch an ogive of the cumulative percentage data in (a) above.

Cumulative percentage ogive for products sales

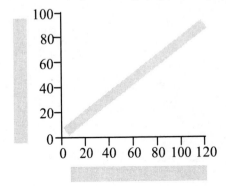

(7 marks)

(c)   Complete the gaps in the following sentences.

An ogive represents a ⬚⬚⬚⬚⬚⬚⬚⬚⬚⬚ distribution.

A decile represents ⬚⬚⬚⬚⬚ of the population.

A percentile represents ⬚⬚⬚⬚⬚ of the population.   **(3 marks)**

(Total: 20 marks)

8   DEPARTMENT STORES

The data below refers to a survey of department stores in the United Kingdom. There were 67 reported cases of staff fraud in the previous five year period.

Range of financial losses	Number of cases	Value of losses
Nil	17	-
Less than £10,000	18	90,000
10,000 – 14,999	11	128,000
15,000 – 19,000	6	108,000
20,000 – 24,999	3	69,000
25,000 – 29,999	4	104,000
30,000 – 59,000	4	200,000
60,000 – 99,000	2	184,000
100,000+	2	500,000
Total	67	1,383,000

Required:

(a)   Calculate the arithmetic mean and median for this data by the most accurate method:

(i)   including all 67 cases: mean = ⬚⬚⬚ ; median = ⬚⬚⬚

(6 marks)

(ii)   excluding the first class of 17 cases: mean = ⬚⬚⬚ ; median = ⬚⬚⬚

(4 marks)

(b)   Complete the gaps in the following points explaining the findings.

●   Arithmetic mean is approximately ⬚⬚⬚ the median in both cases.

●   This is because distribution leans to the ⬚⬚⬚ but has a longer tail to the ⬚⬚⬚ with higher values of the ⬚⬚⬚ .

●   A ⬚⬚⬚ of the frauds committed result in a zero loss.

●   Under such situations arithmetic mean will always be ⬚⬚⬚ than the median.

(4 marks)

(c)   Complete the gaps in the following description of the standard deviation.

The standard deviation is a measure of ⬚⬚⬚ which indicates the ⬚⬚⬚ spread of all data items from the ⬚⬚⬚ .

For ungrouped data the formula is:

SD   =   ⬚⬚⬚

For grouped data the formula is:

SD   =   ▨

A high value for the standard deviation indicates that the data is ▨ dispersed around the ▨ .

A low value indicates that the data is ▨ quite closely around the ▨ .

(6 marks)

(Total: 20 marks)

9   SINBAD LTD

In April 20X9 a survey of customer transaction values was carried out by Sinbad Ltd. The following data was collected.

Transaction value	Number of customers
Below £1	274
£1 - £1.99	518
£2 - £2.99	594
£3 - £3.99	756
£4 - £4.99	386
£5 - £5.99	168
£6 - £6.99	104

Required:

From the above data:

(a)   The mean transaction value is ▨   **(5 marks)**

(b)   The standard deviation is ▨   **(5 marks)**

(c)   Complete the gaps in the following comparison to last year's survey which showed a mean of £2.89 and a standard deviation of £1.39.

The mean amount spent by customers has ▨ by ▨ pence and the standard deviation by ▨ pence.

The ▨ in the mean denotes that the ▨ has risen over the period and the ▨ in standard deviation indicates that there is more ▨ in the level of purchaser.

(5 marks)

(Total: 15 marks)

10   MANAGER'S REPORT

At the close of business on the last working day of each month, the Manager of a branch of a bank requires his staff to produce a brief summary of the account balances. These monthly figures are intended to form the basis of the Manager's quarterly report which is then used by the head office for planning purposes. To provide this information, the accounts of a randomly selected sample of 100 customers are examined. The details for one month are shown in the table below.

Account balance £000	Class mid-point x	Class frequency f	fx	fx²
0 to less than 2	1	10		
2 to less than 4	3	40	A	B
4 to less than 6	5	30		
6 to 8	7	20		
Total (Σ)		100	420	2,100

Required:

(a)   Fill in the appropriate numerical value as indicated by the letters in the table above:

A   **(2 marks)**

B   **(2 marks)**

(b)   The arithmetic mean of the account balance is   .... **(2 marks)**

(c)   The standard deviation of the account balance is   .... **(2 marks)**

(d)   Answer the question below:

(i)   From the data given in the table above, construct a cumulative 'less than' frequency ogive. **(2 marks)**

Summary of the end-of-day account balances

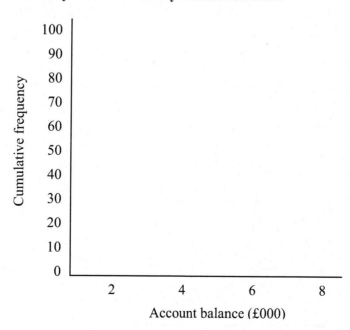

(ii)   The median of the account balances is   **(2 marks)**

(iii)   The semi-interquartile range of the account balance is   **(2 marks)**

(e)   Giving your reasons, explain whether the mean and standard deviation, or the median and semi-interquartile range, would be the most appropriate summary measures for this set of data. *(Do not exceed 50 words.)*   **(3 marks)**

(Total: 17 marks)

PROBABILITY

11   PERISHABLE COMMODITIES

A wholesaler buys a perishable commodity at £30 per case and sells it at £60 per case. Daily demand is uncertain, and any unsold cases at the end of the day are given without charge to a local charity and so represent a loss to the wholesaler.

Past records suggest that the pattern of demand is as follows:

Daily demand	
Number of cases	Probability
20	0.20
21	0.40
22	0.30
23	0.10

The wholesaler wishes to know the amounts of stock to be purchased each day in order to maximise long-run profitability.

Required:

(a)   Complete the following conditional and expected profit tables for the commodity.

Stock purchased	Sales demand			
	20 £	21 £	22 £	23 £
20				
21				
22				
23				

Sales demand	Probability	Stock purchased			
		20 EV	21 EV	22 EV	23 EV
20	0.2				
21	0.4				
22	0.3				
23	0.1				

(14 marks)

(b) Complete the gaps in the following advice to the wholesaler.

Given that the wholesaler is seeking to ░░░░░░░ profits, he will order ░░░ cases per day which will yield an expected profit of ░░░░, the highest of the available alternatives.

(3 marks)

(c) Are the following assumptions by the wholesaler valid or not?

	Valid	*Not valid*

If there was no prior knowledge of the demand pattern, the wholesaler might make the following assumptions:

- If less cases are bought, they could be purchased at a lower price.   ☐   ☐

- Price could be held constant up to a certain time of day and then lowered to clear perishable stock.   ☐   ☐

- To operate a cautious purchasing policy until regular buying patterns were established, eg there may be daily or seasonal fluctuations.   ☐   ☐

(3 marks)

(Total: 20 marks)

12   PORCELAIN MANUFACTURER

A porcelain manufacturer has three assembly lines (X, Y and Z) producing decorative plates. An inspector samples finished plates from the assembly lines in the ratio 1X:2Y:3Z.

Analysis of past inspection records suggests that the defective rates from the assembly lines are:

X	Y	Z
5%	10%	30%

During a shift the inspector examines 240 plates.

Required:

(a) Calculate how many plates the inspector examines from each assembly line.

Line X   ░░░░░░░

Line Y   ░░░░░░░

Line Z   ░░░░░░░   **(3 marks)**

(b) The probability that a plate sampled is defective is ░░░░░░░   **(6 marks)**

(c) The probability that a plate sampled comes from Assembly Line Z, given that it is defective, is ░░░░░░░   **(4 marks)**

(d) Complete the gaps in the following description of what is meant by 'mutually exclusive' and 'independent' events.

Mutually exclusive events cannot happen ░░░░░░░, eg if you toss a coin once getting a head or a tail i░░░░░░░. It is either one or the other.

An independent event is one that, if it happens it has ░░░░░░░ on another event occurring, eg ░░░░░░░ and ░░░░░░░.

(4 marks)

(Total: 17 marks)

13 TRAVEL AGENCY I

A travel agent keeps a stock of holiday brochures. Currently there is a total of 500 brochures in stock as follows: 285 for European holidays, 90 for American holidays, 110 for Asian holidays and 15 for African holidays. A brochure is selected at random.

Required:

The probability that:

(a) a European brochure is selected is

(b) an African brochure is NOT selected is   **(3 marks)**

(c) neither an American nor an Asian brochure is selected is   **(3 marks)**

(d) either a European or an Asian brochure is selected is   **(3 marks)**

(e) Complete the gaps in the following:

The expected value EV is a probability weighted average of the value of each outcome where:

$EV = \sum px$ where $x =$ _____ $p =$ _____   **(2 marks)**

(f) Give three advantages of using expected values in decision making.

Your answer in each case should not exceed 15 words.

(3 marks)

(g) Give three disadvantages of using expected values in decision making.

Your answer in each case should not exceed 15 words.

(3 marks)

(Total: 20 marks)

14   SAMPLING THEORY

(a)   Complete the gaps in the following description of:

- Simple random sampling

- Stratified sampling

- Quota sampling

SIMPLE RANDOM SAMPLING

This is a method in which ▨▨▨ member of a population has an ▨▨▨ chance of being chosen in the sample. One way this can be achieved is by numbering every member of a population, putting their numbers into a hat; in practice this would be carried out by computer. If a sample is to be fair, it is necessary for some sort of ▨▨▨ sampling to be used.

STRATIFIED SAMPLING

If our population consists of a collection of different ▨▨▨ , then we can extend the idea of random sampling so that our population is split into these sub-▨▨▨ and a random sample taken from the different sub-▨▨▨ . If a population has sub-▨▨▨ within it, then this is the most reliable method of sampling.

QUOTA SAMPLING

In this method you specify how many ▨▨▨ you want to sample, ie set a quota, then collect data from anyone or anything that ▨▨▨ until the quota is filled. This method is widely used by interviewers ▨▨▨ is the ▨▨▨ accurate of sampling methods.

(9 marks)

(b)   A random sample of process times in minutes has a mean of 120 and a variance of 400. The sample size is 100 observations. Over what symmetrical range does 95% of the population lie?

▨▨▨ to ▨▨▨ minutes

(6 marks)

(Total: 15 marks)

15   TELEPHONE SALES STAFF

A company employs a large number of telephone sales staff who are based in their homes all over the country. A statistical investigation has been carried out on their work over a period. This produced a frequency distribution showing the number of sales people and the number of positive enquiries resulting from their calls.

The frequency distribution has been partially analysed, with results as follows:

Σf =   1,000

Σfx =   30,000

Σfx^2 =   994,400

where f = number of sales people

and x = the midpoints of the class intervals of positive enquiries.

Tests show that the distribution approximates to normal.

Required:

(a)   The mean number of enquiries per sales person is   **(2 marks)**

(b)   The standard deviation of enquiries is   **(5 marks)**

(c)   The probability of a sales person producing more than 40 enquiries is

                                                                      (4 marks)

(d)   The probability of a sales person producing between 15 and 25 enquiries is

                                                                      (6 marks)

(e)   Give two types of information the company would gain from this type of investigation.

> *Your answer to each point should not exceed 15 words.*

                                                                      (3 marks)

(Total: 20 marks)

FINANCIAL MATHEMATICS

16   RESERVE FUNDS AND MORTGAGES

(a)   In exactly three years from now a company will have to replace capital equipment which will then cost £500,000. The managers have decided to set up a reserve fund into which 12 equal sums will be put at quarterly intervals with the first one being made now. The rate of compound interest is 2% per quarter. The sums required for the reserve fund are   **(7 marks)**

(b)   A fixed interest 10 year £100,000 mortgage is to be repaid by 40 equal quarterly payments in arrears. Interest is charged at 3% a quarter on the outstanding part of the debt.

    (i)   The sum to which an investment of £100,000 would grow after 10 years at a quarterly compound interest of 3% is   **(3 marks)**

    (ii)   The quarterly mortgage payment is   **(7 marks)**

    (iii) The effective annual rate of interest on the mortgage is   **(3 marks)**

The sum, S, of a geometric series of N terms, with first term A and common ratio R, is given by:

$$S = \frac{A(R^N - 1)}{(R - 1)}$$

(Total: 20 marks)

17 INTEREST AND COMPOUND INTEREST

(a) Distinguish between simple interest and compound interest.

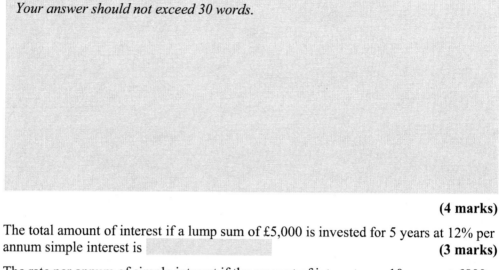

Your answer should not exceed 30 words.

(4 marks)

(b) The total amount of interest if a lump sum of £5,000 is invested for 5 years at 12% per annum simple interest is **(3 marks)**

(c) The rate per annum of simple interest if the amount of interest over 10 years on £800 is £400 is **(3 marks)**

(d) The compound interest on £625 at 4% per annum for 10 years is **(5 marks)**

(e) The sum of money which, if invested now at 5% per annum compound interest, will be worth £10,000 in 10 years' time is **(2 marks)**

(Total: 17 marks)

18 HOSPITAL MAINTENANCE COSTS

The building services department of a hospital has estimated that the maintenance costs over the next 8 years for an existing air conditioner will be as follows:

Year	Estimated cost* £
1	3,000
2	3,500
3	4,000
4	12,000
5	4,000
6	4,500
7	5,000
8	13,000

*The costs are paid at the beginning of each year.

Required:

(a) Using a 6% cost of capital, complete the following present value table of the estimated maintenance costs.

Time period	Cost £	6% discount factor	Discounted cash flow £
0		1	
1			
2			
3			
4			
5			
6			
7			

(6 marks)

Based on the estimated costs, a contract maintenance company has offered to take over the maintenance for the hospital for a fixed annual charge payable at the beginning of each year.

(b) The maximum fixed annual charge the maintenance company could make to the hospital is ▆▆▆▆▆▆▆▆ **(4 marks)**

(c) Briefly discuss the factors which the hospital might consider in deciding whether or not to contract out the maintenance.

Each factor must not exceed 15 words.

(5 marks)

(Total: 15 marks)

19 PRODUCT LIFE CYCLE

A company is planning a new product for which a 10 year life is anticipated. The product is expected to follow a typical life cycle of growth, maturity and decline with a cash flow of £56,000 in year 1. Estimates of cash flows expected from years 2 to 10 are as follows:

Year	Percentage rate of change expected on the **previous year's** cash flow
2	+2
3	+5
4	+10
5	+10
6	+10
7	+5
8	-1
9	-3
10	-5

Assume all cash flows arise at year ends.

Required:

(a)   Complete the following table of cash flow expected in each year.

Year	Cash flow (£)
1	
2	
3	
4	
5	
6	
7	
8	
9	
10	

(5 marks)

(b)   The maximum amount that the company could invest now in the product if it is to meet its target of an 8% return is   **(12 marks)**

(c)   Give three reasons why discounting is carried out in appraising investment decisions.

Your reasons should not each exceed 20 words.

(3 marks)

(Total: 20 marks)

20   LOAN

(a)   A company borrowed £50,000 to buy some new equipment. Interest on this loan is compounded annually at 9%. The company is required to pay off the loan by making a single payment after five years.

In order to have the cash available to make this payment, it has decided that annual payments will be made into a sinking fund that compounds interest annually at 5%. The first payment into the fund will be made one year after the loan was taken out, and the last payment will be made on the day the loan is repaid.

The table below shows how the debt and sinking fund will grow during the five years:

	LOAN			SINKING FUND		
Year end	Interest charged	Outstanding debt		Interest earned	Payment	Amount in fund
	£	£		£	£	£
1				0	13,922.61	13,922.61
2	A					D
3						
4				C		
5		B				

Required:

Write your answers in the boxes below.

Calculate the appropriate numerical value to go in the space indicated by the letters in the table above:

A   **(2 marks)**

B   **(2 marks)**

C   **(3 marks)**

D   **(3 marks)**

(b)   The manager of a sports centre has forecast that the sports centre will need £80,000 in cash in four years' time so that it can buy some new equipment. In order to have the necessary cash available at that date, the Manager has decided to put £X every quarter into a sinking fund. The payments will start immediately (and therefore 17 payments will be made). Interest on the fund will be compounded at 3.5% per quarter.

Required:

Write your answers in the boxes below.

(i) Calculate the value of £X (that is, the quarterly payment into the fund).

> **(4 marks)**

(ii) What is the present value of the £80,000 (assuming an interest rate of 3.5% per quarter)?

> **(2 marks)**

> **(Total: 16 marks)**

Note: A geometric series of terms, with first term A and common ratio R, is denoted by:

$$A + AR + AR^2 + AR^3 + ... + AR^{n-1}$$

The sum of this series is given by: $S_n = \dfrac{A(R^n - 1)}{(R - 1)}$

FORECASTING

21   TRAVEL AGENCY II

A travel agency has kept records of the number of holidays booked and the number of complaints received over the past 10 years. The data is as follows.

Year	1	2	3	4	5	6	7	8	9	10
Number of holidays booked	246	192	221	385	416	279	343	582	610	674
Number of complaints received	94	80	106	183	225	162	191	252	291	310

The agency suspects there is a relationship between the number of bookings and the volume of complaints and wishes to have some method of estimating the number of complaints, given the volume of bookings.

Required:

(a) Complete the following table and use formulae to calculate the coefficients in the regression line y = a + bx using the above data.

x	y	x^2	xy

a =

b =   **(10 marks)**

(b) Using the calculated values to forecast the number of complaints if the number of holidays booked is 750 gives the number of complaints as   **(6 marks)**

(c) State three problems with the usefulness of linear regression for forecasting in this case.

Each point must not exceed 15 words.

(4 marks)

(Total: 20 marks)

22   SALE OF PRODUCT X

Sales of Product X have been recorded for each quarter over the last few years. The data, which have been partially analysed, are as follows:

Year	Quarter	Sales (units)	Sum of fours
20X6	2	40	
	3	53	
			185
	4	74	
			187
20X7	1	18	
			185
	2	42	
			188
	3	51	
			190
	4	77	
			193
20X8	1	20	
			195
	2	45	
			193
	3	53	
			191
	4	75	
20X9	1	18	

Required:

(a)   Complete the analysis of the original data AND calculate the four quarterly moving average trend.
(8 marks)

(b)   Calculate the seasonally-adjusted demand for each quarter, assuming an additive model with the following seasonal factors:

Seasonal factors on trend:

Quarter 1	*Quarter 2*	*Quarter 3*	*Quarter 4*
-28.5	-4.1	+4.3	+28.3

Seasonally-adjusted demand:

Year	*Quarter*	*Sales units*	*Seasonal adjustment*	*Seasonally-adjusted demand*
20X6	2	40		
	3	53		
	4	74		
20X7	1	18		
	2	42		
	3	51		
	4	77		
20X8	1	20		
	2	45		
	3	53		
	4	75		
20X9	1	18		

(8 marks)

(c)   Briefly explain the difference between multiplicative and additive models for producing seasonally-adjusted data.

Your explanation should not exceed 30 words.

(4 marks)

(Total: 20 marks)

23   SALES FORECAST

(a)   The following data shows the number of cash receipts per day for a company over four working weeks.

Week	Day				
	1	*2*	*3*	*4*	*5*
1	8	12	15	10	9
2	10	13	17	15	16
3	17	23	25	21	21
4	26	30	32	34	35

Complete the following table to calculate the trend using five day moving averages.

Week	Day	Receipts		Trend
1	1			
	2			
	3			
	4			
	5			
2	1			
	2			
	3			
	4			
	5			
3	1			
	2			
	3			
	4			
	5			
4	1			
	2			
	3			
	4			
	5			

(6 marks)

(b)   What useful information from the trend could you pass on to the management of this company?

(3 marks)

(c)   What is seasonally-adjusted data? Give two examples where it is used.

(5 marks)

(Total: 14 marks)

ANSWERS TO OBJECTIVE TEST QUESTIONS

BASIC MATHEMATICS

1   B

New price = £2/kg, a reduction of 60p per kg from original price of £2.60. The percentage reduction is thus $\dfrac{60p}{260p} \times 100 = 23.08\%$.

2   C

We know that:

(i)   the selling price is 100% of the price.

(ii)   the profit is 20% on the selling price.

Hence, the cost price must be 100 − 20 = 80% of the selling price.

$$\frac{\text{Cost price}}{80} \times 100 = \text{Selling price}$$

$$\frac{40}{80} \times 100 \qquad = £50$$

As the selling price is £50, and the cost price is £40, then the profit is £(50 − 40) = £10.

3   B

	£	%
Selling price		100
Cost	50	(60)
= Gross profit		40

Selling price is $\dfrac{£50}{60} \times 100 = £83.33$.

4   B

Net earnings= gross earnings − [(gross earnings − 3,500) × 23%]

15,000   = G − 23% G + 3,500 × 23%

77%G   = 15,000 − 805 = 14,195

G   = £18,435

5   B

The values could range from:

$$\frac{4.875}{0.85} \text{ to } \frac{4.885}{0.75}$$

= 5.74 to 6.51

6   A

5x + 3y   = 13   (i)

3x - y   = 12   (ii)

Multiply (ii) by 3

9x - 3y   = 36   (iii)

Add (i) to (iii)

14x   = 49

x   = 3.5

Substitute in (ii)

(3 × 3.5) − y   = 12

10.5 − y   = 12

y   = − 1.5

Therefore x = 3.5 and y = − 1.5.

7   C

Total revenue	= P × Q
Maximum total revenue	= (P × 1.1) × (Q × 1.1)
	= P × Q × 1.21
Maximum rounding error	= 0.21 = 21%

8   B

Telephone cost without VAT	= 10,000 ÷ 1.175 = 8,510.64
Finance	= 8,510.64 × 0.4 × 0.3 = £1,021.28

9   B

£10,000 +/- 5%   = a range from £9,500 to £10,500

£20,000 +/- 10%   = a range from £18,000 to £22,000

Adding the two together means that for a total of £30,000, there can be a range from £27,500 to £32,500. This is a difference of +/- £2,500.

As a percentage, this is:

$$\frac{£2,500}{£30,000} \times 100 = 8.33\%$$

10   B

To find the new totals of fish:

	Number	Increase	Calculation	New total
A	400	10%	= 110/100 × 400	440
B	300	20%	= 120/100 × 300	360
C	200	30%	= 130/100 × 200	260
D	100	40%	= 140/100 × 100	140
			Grand total	1,200

The percentage of D in the lake after a year is therefore

140/1,200 × 100

= 11.66667%

This is closest to 12%.

11   D

$$\frac{X^{10}}{X^{5}} = X^{10} \times X^{-5} = X^{(10-5)} = X^{5}$$

12   B

Minimum value of $\frac{PQ}{N} = \frac{9 \times 900}{11} = £736.36$

13   C

		Ratio			% defective
Machine 1	=	6	× 5	=	30
Machine 2	=	3	× 20	=	60
Machine 3	=	1	× 10	=	10
		10			100

Percentage defects = $\frac{100}{10} = 10$

14   C

39p per kg: 22 kg would cost 22 × 0.39   = £8.58.

Percentage saving from buying in bulk $= \dfrac{7}{8.58} \times 100 = 81.6$

A saving of 100 − 81.6   = 18.4%.

15   D

Revenue, R   = price (P) × quantity (Q)

Maximum price   = 1.2P, maximum quantity = 1.1Q

Minimum price   = 0.8P, minimum quantity = 0.9Q

Maximum revenue = 1.2P × 1.1Q = 1.32PQ (+32%)

Minimum revenue = 0.8P × 0.9Q = 0.72PQ (−28%)

16   A

Minimum possible cost per transaction is:

$$\frac{£10m \text{ less } 6\%}{1m \text{ plus } \frac{1}{2}\%} = \frac{£9.4m}{1.005m} = £9.35$$

17   B

Let X be growth factor

X^6 = 3

X   = 1.2009

Annual percentage growth rate = 20.09%

18   C

From your formula sheet, the formula for compound interest is:

S $= x[\ 1\text{-}r]^n$

Using the information provided:

2      $= 32\ [1 - r]^4$

$\dfrac{2}{32}$ $= [1 - r]^4$

$\sqrt[4]{\dfrac{2}{32}}$ $= 1 - r$

r $= 1 - \dfrac{1}{2}$

       $= \dfrac{1}{2}$ (or 50%)

19   B

$$400 \quad = \quad \sqrt{\frac{2 \times 20 \times 24{,}000}{H}}$$

$$160{,}000 \quad = \quad \frac{960{,}000}{H}$$

$$H \quad = \quad \frac{960{,}000}{160{,}000} = £6$$

20   C

$$S \quad = \quad \frac{A(R^2 - 1)}{(R - 1)}$$

$$\frac{S}{A} \quad = \quad \frac{R^2 - 1}{R - 1} = R + 1$$

$$R \quad = \quad \frac{S}{A} - 1$$

Alternatively:

$$S \quad = \quad \frac{A(R^2 - 1)}{(R - 1)}$$

This is the sum of a GP with 2 terms, common ratio R and first term, A.

Hence $S = A + AR$

$S = A(1 + R)$

$$\frac{S}{A} = 1 + R$$

$$\frac{S}{A} - 1 = R$$

21   C

$£8.792 \times 10^{10} \times 1.53$

$= £13.45176 \times 10^{10}$

$= £13.45176 \times 10^{4}$ millions

$= £134{,}518$ millions

22 **A**

Cost = £500,000

Economic life = 8 years

Residual value = £20,000

$$r = 1 - \sqrt[n]{\frac{D}{V}}$$

$$r = 1 - \sqrt[8]{\frac{20,000}{500,000}} = 33\%$$

$500,000 \times 33\% \quad = £165,000$

$500,000 - 165,000 = £335,000$

23 **C**

Substituting the values into

Sr	$= R^N(Ar + P) - P$
$S \times 0.07$	$= (1.07)^{20}(3,000 \times 0.07 + 500) - 500$
$S \times 0.07$	$= 3.86968 (710) - 500$
$S \times 0.07$	$= 2,747.4728 - 500$
$S \times 0.07$	$= 2,247.4728$
S	$= \dfrac{2,247.4728}{0.07}$
S	$= £32,106.75$

24 **B**

	Max	Min
Wages	1,100	900
Materials	2,400	1,600
Costs	3,500	2,500

Max profits = Max rev – Min costs

= 4,400 – 2,500 = 1,900

Min profits = Min rev – Max costs

= 3,600 – 3,500 = 100

25 **C**

Using a calculator, $2^{-0.75} = 0.5946$

$0.5946^{-7} \qquad = 38.05$

26   A

$x^{1/n}$ is the nth root of x so $x^{1/4}$ would be $\sqrt[4]{x}$

x^{-n} is equal to $\dfrac{1}{x^n}$ so x^{-3} would be $\dfrac{1}{x^3}$

$x^{-3/4}$ is therefore the fourth root of x^{-3}, or $\dfrac{1}{\sqrt[4]{x^3}}$

27   B

$$PV = \frac{1}{0.05} - \frac{1}{0.05 \times 1.05^{20}}$$

$$= 20 - \frac{1}{0.05 \times 2.6533}$$

$$= 20 - 7.5378$$

$$= 12.4622$$

28   C

Book value = $100{,}000X^n$

After 4 years:

$50{,}000 = 100{,}000X^4$

$0.5 = X^4$

$X = 0.8409$

After 5 years, new book value is $50{,}000 \times 0.8409 = £42{,}045$

29   D

$Y = 2X + 4$

$Y = 12 - 2X$

At point of intersection, $2X + 4 = 12 - 2X$

$4X = 8$

$X = 2$

When X = 2, substituting gives Y = 8

30   A

$$R = \frac{2PC}{B(N+1)}$$

$$B(N+1) = \frac{2PC}{R}$$

$$N + 1 = \frac{2PC}{RB}$$

$$N = \frac{2PC}{RB} - 1$$

31   D

$$\frac{(1/1.1)S^2}{1-1/1.1}$$

$$= \frac{S^2/1.1}{1-1/1.1}$$

$$= \frac{S^2/1.1}{(1.1-1)/1.1}$$

$$= \frac{S^2/1.1}{0.1/1.1}$$

$$= S^2/1.1 \times 1.1/0.1$$

$$= S^2/0.1$$

$$= 10S^2$$

32   C

$$C = 6 + 0.5 \times 3$$

$$C = 7.5$$

Therefore cost of sales is $7,500.

33   A

$20,000 \times 0.78 \times 0.78 \times 0.78 = \$9,491$

$20,000 \times 0.82 \times 0.82 \times 0.82 = \$11,027$

34   D

Since TC is less than or equal to $100, $TC \leq \$100$

Since revenue is a minimum of $120, $R \geq \$120$

Since R is larger than TC, $R > TC$

Therefore the answer must be D.

35   D

$$R = \left(\frac{V}{P}\right) + G$$

Rearranging:

$$R - G = \frac{V}{P}$$

$$P = \frac{V}{R - G}$$

36   B

$(y^2)^3$ can also be written as

$y^2 \times y^2 \times y^2$

The multiplication of power terms is given by the general expression.

$A^b \times A^c \times A^d = A^{b+c+d}$

Hence

$y^2 \times y^2 \times y^2 = y^{2+2+2} = y^6$

37   B

A negative power denotes the reciprocal of the corresponding positive power. Thus x^{-1} is the reciprocal of x^1, ie $x^{-1} = \dfrac{1}{x}$.

38   D

Max value of $\dfrac{pq}{n}$ will arise when p and q are at maximum values and n is at a minimum

Max value $= \dfrac{(£10 \times 1.1)(1,000 \times 1.1)}{200 \times 0.9} = £67.22$ which is closest to £67.

39   B

$$\left(x^3\right)^{-4} = \frac{1}{\left(x^3\right)^4} = \frac{1}{x^{12}}$$

40   A

$Y = 7 + X$ and $Y = 9 + 3X$

At intersection:

$7 + X = 9 + 3X$

$-2 = 2X$

$X = -1$

Substituting for X in first equation gives:

$Y = 7 + (-1) = 6$

Co-ordinates are $(-1,6)$

41   D

$$X = \frac{2 \pm \sqrt{(-2)^2 - (4 \times (-24))}}{2}$$

$$= \frac{2 \pm 10}{2}$$

42   A

If X is the undiscounted price:

$$X \times (100 - 5)\% = £228$$

$$\frac{95X}{100} = 228$$

$$X = 228 \times \frac{100}{95}$$

$$= £240$$

43   C

44   D

$$\frac{x^{10}}{x^6} = x^{10} \times x^{-6} = x^{(10-6)} = x^4$$

45   D

This could be done by trial and error but, unless the answer is A or B, it could be very time consuming. Let us start with what we know:

1   The selling price is 100% of the price

2   Profit is 20% of the SP

3   Cost must be 80% of SP

$$\frac{40}{80} \times 100 = SP = £50$$

So unit profit $= 50 - 40 = 10$

So profit on 10 units $= 10 \times 10 = £100$

46   C

$$3x + 4y = 25 \quad (i)$$

$$5x + 3y = 27 \quad (ii)$$

Multiply (i) by 3 and (ii) by 4 to obtain:

$$9x + 12y = 75 \quad (iii)$$

and $20x + 12y = 108 \quad (iv)$

Then (iv) – (iii) gives:

$$11x = 33$$

$$\therefore x = 3$$

Substituting in (i)

$$9 + 4y = 25$$

$$4y = 16$$

$$\therefore y = 4$$

47   A

$81^{-\frac{1}{n}} = 0.3333$

One way of calculating this is by pure guesswork.

Try n =3

$81^{-1/3} = 0.23112$

try n = 4

$81^{-1/4} = 0.3333$

48   B

Using the formula $V=X(I+r)^n$

Where	V	= amount at end of period
	X	= original sum
	r	= interest rate
	n	= time period

Then $9{,}625.60 = X(1 +(-0.2))^4$

$9{,}625.6 = X(0.8)^4$

$9{,}625.6 = 0.4096X$

$X = \dfrac{9{,}625.6}{0.4096}$

$= 23{,}500$

49   A

Firstly you need to remove the VAT, ie

$£24.99 \times \dfrac{100}{117.5} = £21.26809$

and then increase this figure by 15%

$21.26809 \times \dfrac{115}{100} = £24.4583$

$\approx £24.46$

50   D

Remember that when a power is raised to a power, the two powers are multiplied together, so $\dfrac{1}{4} \times 4 = 1$, and $x^1 = x$ [anything to the power of one = the original number].

51   False

Selling price   = £36.78

This is 118% of the price (as the sales tax = 18%).

$\therefore$ Selling price excluding tax $= \dfrac{100}{118} \times 36.78$

                            = £31.17

$\therefore$ New price after 20% reduction

                          $= (100 - 20)\% \times 31.17$

                          = £24.94 (to two decimal places)

52   x = 3.5, y = -1.5

     x   y

     3.5   -1.5

$10x + 6y$ $= 26$ (i)

$6x - 2y$ $= 24$ (ii)

Multiply (ii) by 3:

$18x - 6y$ $= 72$ (iii)

(i) plus (iii) gives:

$28x$ $= 98$

x $= 3.5$

Substituting into (ii):

$(6 \times 3.5) - 2y$ $= 24$

$21 - 2y$ $= 24$

$- 2y$ $= 24 - 21$

$- 2y$ $= 3$

y $= \dfrac{3}{-2}$

                 $= -1.5$

53   D

If $\dfrac{13}{30}$ have blond hair, that means that $30 - 13 = 17$ do not have blond hair.

$\dfrac{17}{30} = 0.5666666$

= 0.5667 (to four decimal places)

Remember that when giving an answer to four decimal places (or 2, 3, 5 etc) you need to round up if the next number is > 5 and down if the next number is < 5.

54   x = -14, y = -10

y = 4 + x   (i)

x = 6 + 2y   (ii)

Equation (ii) can be rearranged as:

2y = x – 6   (iii)

Multiplying (i) by 2 gives:

2y = 8 + 2x   (iv)

(iv) – (iii):

0 = 14 + x

Then x = – 14

Solving for y in (i):

y = 4 – 14

Then y = – 10. Hence the lines intersect where x = –14 and y = –10

55   ± 5

$$y^2 \quad = x^2 - 3x + 25$$
$$y^2 \quad = 3^2 - (3 \times 3) + 25$$
$$y^2 \quad = 9 - 9 + 25$$
$$\quad = 25$$
$$y \quad = \pm 5$$

56   21%

Box contains A units

Price = £B per unit

The maximum rounding error if A is rounded to ± 10% is 110% × A or 1.1 A.

The maximum rounding error if B is rounded to ± 10% is 110% × B or 1.1 B.

Total revenue from the boxes   = A × B

∴ Total rounding error   = 1.1 A × 1.1 B

                                  = 1.21 AB

as a percentage, this   = 21%

57   304

If the average journey was 194 miles, then $\dfrac{123 + 268 + x + 302 + 99 + 186 + y}{7} = 194$

If x = 4y, then:

$$\frac{5y + 978}{7} = 194$$

5y + 978   = 194 × 7

5y + 978   = 1,358

$$5y \quad = 1,358 - 978$$

$$= 380$$

$$y \quad = \frac{380}{5} = 76$$

The value of y is 76

$$\text{Since } x \quad = 4y$$

$$x \quad = 4 \times 76$$

$$= 304$$

58 **£15.75, £12.60**

Original ratio is 4:5

Mirjana's share is $\frac{4}{9}$ of total, ie $\frac{4}{9}$ = £7.

Then $\frac{1}{9} \quad = £\frac{7}{4}$

$$= £1.75$$

So the total sum of money = $9 \times £1.75 = £15.75$

If the ratio had been 5:4, then:

$$\frac{5}{9} \quad = £7$$

so $\frac{1}{9} = £\frac{7}{5}$

$$= £1.40$$

Total sum would be $9 \times £1.40 = £12.60$

59 **x = -12 or 25, y = -25 or 12**

$$x^2 + y^2 \quad = 769 \quad \text{(i)}$$

$$x - y \quad = 13 \quad \text{(ii)}$$

$$\text{so } y \quad = x - 13 \quad \text{(iii)}$$

Substituting in (i) we have:

$$x^2 + (x - 13)^2 \quad = 769$$

$$x^2 + (x - 13)(x - 13) \quad = 769$$

$$x^2 + (x^2 - 13x - 13x + 169) \quad = 769$$

$$2x^2 - 26x + 169 \quad = 769$$

$$2x^2 - 26x - 600 \quad = 0$$

Dividing by 2 throughout gives:

$$x^2 - 13x - 300 \quad = 0$$

Solve this quadratic equation using the formula:

$$x = \frac{-b \pm \sqrt{b^2 - (4ac)}}{2a}$$

Then $x = \dfrac{-(-13) \pm \sqrt{13^2 - (4 \times 1 \times (-300))}}{2 \times 1}$

$$= \frac{13 \pm \sqrt{1,369}}{2}$$

$$= \frac{13 + 37}{2} \text{ or } \frac{13 - 37}{2}$$

$$= 25 \text{ or } -12$$

Using (iii):

If $x = 25$,   If $x = -12$

    $y = 25 - 13$ $y = -12 - 13$

       $= 12$ $= -25$

60   **B**

Bread	= 50p per kilogram
Bread in bulk	= £11 per 25 kg bag

so per kg this $= \dfrac{£11}{25}$

                      $= 44$ pence

The saving is therefore:

$50 - 44$ $= 6$ pence/kilo

As a percentage, this $= \dfrac{6}{50} \times 100$

                             $= 12\%$

61   **5**

$(5^{0.25})^4$

$= 5^{(0.25 \times 4)}$

$= 5^1$

$= 5$

62   £0.95

Servicing two million transactions = £2 million.

A minimum cost per transaction is where the maximum number of transactions occurs at the minimum cost.

Maximum transactions   = 2,000,000 × 1.005

                                        = 2,010,000

Minimum cost   = £2,000,000 × 0.95

                                        = 1,900,000

Therefore the minimum cost

$$= \frac{1,900,000}{2,010,000}$$

$$= 0.945274$$

≈ £0.95 (to two decimal places)

63   C

$$(x^{-0.75})^{-7} \quad = \quad x^{(-0.75 \times -7)}$$

$$= \quad \mathbf{X^{5.25}}$$

When x = 2, expression = $2^{5.25}$ = 38.05

64   B

The volume of a rectangular box   =   length × height × depth

Here, volume   =   2a × a × a   = $2a^3$

$2a^3$ =   1,458

a^3 =   729

a   = $\sqrt[3]{729}$

a   =   9

65   C

$(x^2)^3$ = x^6

$\dfrac{x^6}{x^5}$ =   x

66   B

Let the selling price excluding VAT be x. Then:

1.125x   =   84p

x   = $\dfrac{84}{1.125}$ = 74.667

ie selling price excluding VAT = 74.667, ie 75p to nearest pence.

Selling price including new VAT rate is:

75p × 1.175 = 88.125, ie 88p to nearest pence.

67   C

$$100 = \sqrt{\frac{2 \times D \times 10}{6 \times 0.2}}$$

$$100^2 = \frac{20D}{1.2}$$

$$20D = 12,000$$

$$D = 600$$

68   B

Price = £298 including VAT

Cost of article excluding VAT = $\frac{£298}{1.175}$ = £253.62

69   C

$$\frac{(x^3)^3}{x^7} = \frac{x^9}{x^7} = x^2$$

When x = 5, expression = 25

70   A

Selling price of £90.68 = 119% of pre-tax price

Selling price excluding VAT = $\frac{100}{119}$ × £90.68 = £76.20

20% of £76.20 = £15.24

So new price after 20% reduction = £76.20 - £15.24 = £60.96

71   B

$$(x^8)^{-4} = x^{-32} = \frac{1}{x^{32}}$$

72   B

Increase in price = £53.99 - £45.99 = £8

Increase is £8 on £45.99 (original price), ie $\frac{8.00}{45.99}$ × 100% = 17.39508%

So answer is either A or B. However, 17.39508 is closer to 17.40.

73   B

Original price	=	£56.99
New price	=	£52.49
Price reduction	=	£4.50

Then percentage reduction is $\dfrac{£4.50}{£56.99} \times 100 = 7.89612\%$

Again, we choose between A and B, but answer is closer to 7.90%.

74   B

In this example the power are multiplied together. So:

$(x^3)^4$ becomes x^{12}

75   C

Total expenditure		=	£30,151
Costs:			
100 units × £50		=	£5,000
150 units		=	£8,250
Next batch		=	£11,200
Sub-total		=	£24,450
Final 100 cost	£30,151 - £24,450		= £5,701
So unit cost	=	x	= £57.01

76   D

Expenditure in total	=	£469.80
Product A: 20 × £7.84	=	£156.80
Product B: 10 × £8.20	=	£82.00
Product C: 12 × £8.50	=	£102.00
		£340.80

Therefore buyer spends   £469.80 - £340.80 = £129.00 on Product D.

Each case of Product D costs £8.60 ∴ he buys $\dfrac{129.00}{8.60}$ = 15 cases.

If there are 12 items in each case of Product D, buyer purchases 15 × 12 = 180 items.

77   D

$$(x^{\frac{1}{8}})^8 = x^{(\frac{1}{8} \times 8)} = x^1 = x$$

78   A

Original selling price	=	£27.50
Year 1 increase by 5%	=	£28.875
Year 2 increase by 6%	=	£30.6075
ie selling price at end of year 2 was		£30.61
At end of year 3 selling price was		£29.69, a reduction of 92 pence

Hence, percentage price charge is $\dfrac{-0.92}{£30.61} \times 100 = -3\%$

79   C

$y \quad = \quad a + bx$

Using given values:

$491 \quad = \quad 234 + 20b$

$257 \quad = \quad 20b$

$b \quad = \quad 12.85$

80   C

$\dfrac{a^{2x}}{a^{2y}}$

$= a^{(2x-2y)}$

$= a^{2(x-y)}$

81   B

$\dfrac{QH}{2} \quad = \quad \dfrac{DS}{Q}$

$\dfrac{Q^2H}{2} = \quad DS$

$Q^2H \quad = \quad 2DS$

$Q^2 \quad = \quad \dfrac{2DS}{H}$

$\sqrt{Q^2} \quad = \quad \sqrt{\dfrac{2DS}{H}}$

$Q \quad = \quad \sqrt{\dfrac{2DS}{H}}$

82   D

$$P = 40 + 11x - 2x^2$$

When $P = 0$

$$0 = 40 + 11x - 2x^2$$

Rearranging the equation:

$$2x^2 - 11x - 40 = 0$$

ie $(2x + 5)(x - 8) = 0$

$$\therefore x = -\frac{5}{2} = -2.5 \text{ or } x = 8$$

83   C

$$3x + 2y = 6 \text{ (i)}$$

$$x - 2y = 2 \text{ (ii)}$$

(i) and (ii) gives:

$$4x = 8$$

$$\therefore x = 2$$

Substitute into (i):

$$6 + 2y = 6$$

$$2y = 0$$

$$\therefore y = 0$$

Solution is $(2, 0)$

SUMMARISING AND ANALYSING DATA

84   A

Quarter	'Real' sales
1	$\frac{109}{100} \times 100 = 109.0$
2	$\frac{120}{110} \times 100 = 109.1$
3	$\frac{132}{121} \times 100 = 109.1$
4	$\frac{145}{133} \times 100 = 109.0$

The 'real' series is approximately constant and keeping up with inflation.

85 **A**

Mean speed $= \dfrac{\text{Total distance travelled}}{\text{Total time taken}}$

Total distance travelled $= 20 + 10 = 30$ miles

Total time taken for 20 miles at 30 mph plus 10 miles at 60 mph

$\text{Time} = \dfrac{\text{Distance}}{\text{Speed}}$

Then total time taken $= \dfrac{20}{30} + \dfrac{10}{60}$

$= 0.667 + 0.167$

$= 0.83$ hr

mean speed $= \dfrac{30}{0.83} = 36$ mph

86 **D**

This question can be solved algebraically. The information that is given should first be listed.

10 units @ 50p $= £5.00$

10 units @ 70p $= £7.00$

20 units @ Xp $= £0.2X$

Total number of units $= 10 + 10 + 20 = 40$ units

The mean purchase price $= 80p$

As $\dfrac{\text{The total cost of the units}}{\text{Number of units}} = \text{Mean price}$

Hence:

$\dfrac{5 + 7 + 0.2X}{40} = 0.8$

$5 + 7 + 0.2X = 0.8 \times 40$

$12 + 0.2X = 32$

Then $0.2X = 32 - 12 = 20$

Hence X $= \dfrac{20}{0.2} = 100$

87 **C**

Width is 0.75 of standard; hence score needs to be divided by that factor, ie $\dfrac{21}{0.75} = 28$

88 **C**

In ascending order: 8, 9, 11, 12, 14, 15, 17, 21, 24, 34

The median value is halfway between the values of the 5th and 6th items, ie 14.5

89   C

Price (£)	Total (£)	Number
10.00	400	40
12.50	500	40
11.00	550	50
12.00	600	50
	2,050	180

Average price = $\dfrac{£2,050}{180}$ = £11.39

90   B

Width is 1.25 × standard ∴ height must be divided by this factor, ie $\dfrac{80}{1.25} = 64$

91   B

Rearranging in ascending order:

17, 19, 21, 21, 24, 26, 27, 31, 32, 42

Median age = age of middle item

= average age of 5th and 6th people

= average of 24 and 26 = 25 years

92   B

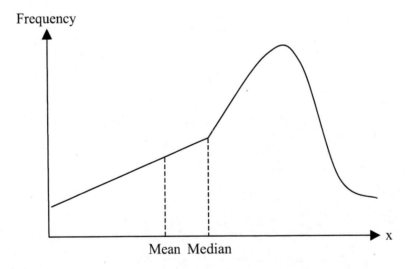

In a negatively skewed distribution the mean is smaller than the median.

93   C

In ascending order

7, 8, 13, 14, 28, 33, 42, 51, 69 plus x

Median is middle item, which is 28, with 14, 33 or x.

$$\frac{28+14}{2} \neq 29 \text{ and } \frac{28+33}{2} \neq 29$$

Hence median $= 29 = \dfrac{28+x}{2}$

$58 - 28 = x$

$x = 30$

94   D

10° represents £250,000

Then 360° represents $£\dfrac{250,000}{10} \times 360 = £9m$

95   B

This is the defining rationale of a histogram

96   C

97   B

List the given weights in ascending order:

53   59   69   84   94   97   105   and   x

The median of 8 numbers is the mean of the middle two.

Median is $78 \neq \dfrac{69+84}{2}$ and $78 \neq \dfrac{84+94}{2}$

Hence $78 = \dfrac{84+x}{2}$, ie x = 72

98   C

This is the definition of systematic sampling.

99   B

Secondary data is used for one purpose, although it was originally collected for another purpose.

100   C

Quota sampling involves the sampler filling predetermined categories of items, eg an interviewer might be told to interview 5 men aged above 60 and 10 women aged above 70. The interviewer then finds these quota members in whatever way he wishes. No list of the items in the population (the sampling frame) is required.

101   B

Mean $\bar{x} = \dfrac{2+4+6+8+10}{5} = \dfrac{30}{5} = 6$ orders

Standard deviation $\sigma = \sqrt{\dfrac{\sum(x-\bar{x})^2}{n}}$

$= \sqrt{\dfrac{(-4)^2 + (-2)^2 + 0 + 2^2 + 4^2}{5}}$

$= \sqrt{\dfrac{16 + 4 + 0 + 4 + 16}{5}}$

$= \sqrt{\dfrac{40}{5}}$

$= \sqrt{8} = 2.83$ orders

102   A

Mode = most commonly occurring item = 55 marks

103   B

Median = middle item when the data is ranked in order.

37, 45, 55, 55, 56, 64, 70, 72, 86

⬆

Median

104   D

Co-efficient of variation $= \dfrac{\sigma}{\bar{x}} \times 100\%$

It thus records the size of the standard deviation relative to the size of the mean, ie it is a measure of relative dispersion.

105   D

A simple bar chart would show five bars illustrating the different salaries in different regions.

106   A

Arithmetic mean $= \dfrac{(5 \times 0 + 10 \times 1 + 10 \times 2 + 20 \times 3 + 5 \times 4 + 0 \times 5)}{50}$

$\qquad\qquad\quad = \dfrac{110}{50}$

$\qquad\qquad\quad = 2.2$

107   B

Cumulative frequency curve can be used to find the median. Halfway up the vertical axis, read across and project down.

108   B

Simple random sampling always eliminates selection bias but does not guarantee a representative sample.

109   D

Accountant first stratifies the invoices according to value and then selects randomly. Sampling method is stratified.

110   B

$$\text{All items index} = \frac{(50 \times 140) + (30 \times 130) + (20 \times 120)}{100}$$

$$= 133$$

111   A

Median will be 15 if it lies between values 14 and 16. Hence value $20 + X$ must be greater than 15, ie X cannot equal -5.

112   A

All items = food + non-food

127×10	$= (? \times 3) + (130 \times 7)$
1270	$= 3? + 910$
$3?$	$= 1270 - 910$
$3?$	$= 360$
$?$	$= \dfrac{360}{3}$
	$= 120$

113   D

Option A is not random – it is a stratified sample.

Option B selects only those who are in a class – so it is NOT random.

Option C, again, is not random as it only selects from 10% of colleges (and therefore does not include home study, or the other 90%).

114 B

The calculation is as follows:

	£
Sales for first five months (5 × £8,200)	41,000
Sales for last four months (4 × £8,500)	34,000
	75,000
Total sales for the year	102,000
∴ Sales for missing three months	27,000

$$\therefore \text{Average sales} = £27,000 \div 3$$
$$= £9,000 \text{ per month}$$

115 A

$$x \times \frac{112}{100} = 140$$

$$\therefore x = \frac{140}{1.12} = 125$$

116 A

The quartile deviation is defined as half of the difference between the upper and lower quartiles.

Order the set, ie 31, 38, 40, 42, 43, 60, 68. The median value is 42, the lower quartile value is 38 and the upper quartile value is 60.

The quartile deviation is therefore

$$\frac{60-38}{2} = \frac{22}{2} = 11$$

117 B

$$1999 \text{ weekly pay} = \frac{144}{125} \times £200 = £230 \text{ per week (to the nearest £).}$$

118 B

The median is the middle item, found by rearranging the hours worked into ascending order.

35   35   36   36   36   (37)   38   40   40   42   43

119   C

If you don't feel very confident with questions like this, you could approach it step-by-step.

$1999 = 120$

$$2000 = 120 \times \frac{110}{100} = 132$$

$$2001 = 132 \times \frac{110}{100} = 145.2$$

$$2002 = 145.2 \times \frac{110}{100} = 159.72$$

Alternatively, as the increase is 10% over three years, you could calculate:

$120 \times (1.1)^3 = 159.72$

120   D

121   C

This question is exceedingly straightforward, even if it seems complicated at first. All you need to do is express the standard deviation as a percentage of performance criteria marks.

Therefore $\dfrac{2}{20} \times 100 = 10\%$

122   C

Run through some quick calculations to work this out, eg:

Mean 1 $= \dfrac{2+5+5+12}{4} = 6$

Mean 2 $= \dfrac{1+3+5+8+8}{5} = 5$

Median 1 $= \dfrac{5+5}{2} = 5$

Median 2 $= 5$

123   C

The coefficient of variation = standard deviation ÷ mean

Therefore $= \dfrac{3}{12}$

As a percentage, this $= \dfrac{3}{12} \times 100 = 25\%$

124   A

$$\frac{286 + 192 + x + 307 + 185 + y + 94}{7} = 267$$

Rearranging, $x + y = (267 \times 7) - 1{,}064$

$$= 805$$

We also know that $y = 4x$

Substituting this value of y into the equation gives:

$5x \quad = 805$

$\therefore x \quad = 161$

125   C

Large standard deviation indicates data is spread out about the mean - hence choose histogram **C**.

126   D

Annual sales are 200 each year, ie are static.

Q4 has highest sales in all 3 years.

Mean sales for Q2 = 200 ÷ 4 = 50

Mean quarterly sales for all 3 years is 600 ÷ 12 = 50

Therefore all 3 statements are correct.

127   C

Commodity	Price relative (Yr 2/Yr 1)	Weighting
A	$\frac{11}{10}$ = 1.1	10
B	$\frac{24}{20}$ = 1.2	1
C	$\frac{52}{50}$ = 1.04	5
D	$\frac{105}{100}$ = 1.05	4
		$\overline{20}$

$$\therefore \text{Price index} = \left(\frac{10}{20} \times 1.1\right) + \left(\frac{1}{20} \times 1.2\right) + \left(\frac{5}{20} \times 1.04\right) + \left(\frac{4}{20} \times 1.05\right)$$

$$= 0.55 + 0.06 + 0.26 + 0.21 = 1.08$$

$$= 108 \text{ expressed as a percentage.}$$

128 C

Price relative $= \dfrac{1.75}{1.40} \times 100 = 125$

129 C

Inflation index rose from 120 to 240, ie doubled.

Purchase price is $75,000; no tax paid up to $150,000

Tax $= 0.4 \times 100,000 = \$40,000$

130 A

Increase in money wages $= (115 - 100)/100 = 15\%$

Increase in inflation $\quad = (210 - 180)/180 = 16.7\%$

Therefore (i) is true.

However (ii) is not true as the index has increased by 5 points each year but as a percentage this is less than 5%.

131 B

Real wages 2001 $\quad = 115 \times 180/210$

$\qquad\qquad\qquad\quad = 98.57$

As this is below the 1998 real wage index of 100, real wages have decreased by approximately $100 - 98.57 = 1.43\%$

132 C

We have ten variables of which eight are known and two are unknown and the arithmetic mean of the 10 numbers is 20.

So we can write

$$\frac{Y + 15 + 22 + 14 + 21 + 15 + 20 + 18 + 27 + Y}{10} = 20$$

$$\frac{2Y + 152}{10} = 20$$

Then $2Y + 152 \quad = 200$

$2Y \qquad\qquad\quad = 48$

$Y \qquad\qquad\quad = 24$

133 D

Let height be h. Then $\dfrac{5}{8} h = 400$

Therefore $\dfrac{1}{8} h = \dfrac{400}{5} = 80$

Therefore $h = 8 \times 80 = 640$

134   C

In the base year, the price $= \dfrac{100}{87} \times £490$

$= £563.2183$

$\approx £563.22$

135   C

The highest profit must be where the buying is the lowest, but the selling price is the highest, therefore

Sell   Buy   Garments   Profit

$(£23 – £8)   \times   100   =   £1,500$

The lowest profit is where the buying price is the highest and selling lowest.

$(£17 – £12)   \times   100   =   £500$

$\therefore$ the range of possible profit $= £1,500 - £500$

$= £1,000$

136   D

This uses a very similar concept to the answer above.

	Selling price	*Unit cost*	*Sales*	*Contribution*
Highest	$(7 \times 1.15) = 8.05$	$(5 \times 0.9) = 4.50$	$(40,000 \times 1.2) = 48,000$	170,400
Lowest	$(7 \times 0.85) = 5.95$	$(5 \times 1.1) = 5.50$	$(40,000 \times 0.8) = 32,000$	14,400
			Range	156,000

137   D

If O = overheads, M = Materials and W = Wages,

then we are given: O = 4W and W = 2M

Therefore M= 0.5 W

Now 12% + M + O + W = 100%

12 + 0.5W + 4W + W = 100%

12 + 5.5W = 100%

5.5W = 88%,

therefore $W = \dfrac{88}{5.5} = 16$

Overhead = 4W = 64

The pie segment of overhead is therefore 64% of 360°

$= \dfrac{64}{100} \times 360$

$= 230.4°$

$\approx 230°$

138   False

An ogive is a cumulative frequency distribution.

139   D

The median is the value of the middle in a distribution once all the items have been arranged in order of magnitude. Putting these numbers (excluding x) in order:

5,   14,   17,   23, (34,) 39,   56,   70,   78

The median (without x) is 34.

Since we know the median = 33

$$33 = \frac{x + 34}{2}$$

$$66 = x + 34$$

$$66 - 34 = x$$

$$32 = x$$

140   29.5

The mean is calculated as the total value of the items divided by the total number of items.

$$\frac{\text{Total value}}{\text{Total in number}} = \frac{23 + 45 + 9 + 53 + 71 + 26 + 31 + 14 + 7 + 16}{10}$$

$$= \frac{295}{10}$$

$$\text{Mean} = 29.5$$

141   126 cm

$$\text{Mean} = \frac{\text{Total value}}{\text{Total in number}}$$

$$120 = \frac{130 + ... + x}{10}$$

$$120 = \frac{1{,}074 + x}{10}$$

$$1{,}200 = 1{,}074 + x$$

$$x = 1{,}200 - 1{,}074$$

$$x = 126 \text{ cm}$$

142   67

The mode is the value that occurs most frequently amongst all the items in the distribution.

Mark	Frequency
49	I
51	I
55	I
56	I
61	I
67	II
68	I
78	I
82	I
89	I

so the most frequent value is 67, having occurred twice.

143   60

The median is the middle item.

Putting the marks in order we have:

42 52 55 55 59 (60) 62 67 72 78 87

∴ Median = 60

144   32

$$\text{Variance} = \frac{\Sigma(x - \overline{x})^2}{n}$$

$$\overline{x} = \frac{\Sigma x}{n}$$

$$= \frac{4 + 8 + 12 + 16 + 20}{5}$$

$$= \frac{60}{5}$$

ie $\overline{x} = 12$

Then:

x	$(x - \overline{x})$	$(x - \overline{x})^2$
4	− 8	64
8	− 4	16
12	0	0
16	4	16
20	8	64
		$\Sigma = 160$

$$\text{Variance} \quad = \frac{\Sigma(x - \overline{x})^2}{n}$$

$$= \frac{160}{5}$$

$$= 32$$

145 A

The coefficient of variation is used to measure relative dispersion by expressing the standard deviation as a percentage of the mean.

146 True

A histogram is a special form of bar chart.

147 10.0

If the standard width is 5 units, the width of 7.5 is $1.5 \times$ the standard.

Remember that a histogram shows the relationship of rectangles to the frequencies by reference to the area, so we need to divide the frequency of 15 by 1.5 to find the adjusted height.

$$\frac{15}{1.5} = 10$$

to one decimal place this is 10.0

148 £180

Price index in 2000 = 146

Price index in 1996 = 122

$\therefore$ to find the 2000 weekly pay, we need to divide the 2000 price index by the 1996 price index and multiply by the 1996 pay.

ie $\dfrac{146}{122} \times £150 \quad = £179.5082$

$$\approx £180 \text{ (to the nearest £)}$$

149 The standard deviation will increase by 7%, and the coefficient of variation will be unaltered.

Since the mean increases, the standard deviation will logically increase (remember the formula $\dfrac{\Sigma(x - \overline{x})^2}{n}$). Since the coefficient of variation = $\dfrac{\text{Standard deviation} \times 100}{\text{Mean}}$, this will become $\dfrac{\text{Standard deviation} + 7\%}{\text{Mean} + 7\%}$, and this will not alter.

150   £135

Current price = £175

Current index = 130

To find the price in the base year, you need to use $\dfrac{\text{Base index}}{\text{Current index}} \times \text{current price}$

$= \dfrac{100}{130} \times 175$

$= 134.6154$

$\approx £135$ (to the nearest £).

151   True

Remember that secondary data is data which has been collected for some other enquiry than the one of immediate interest.

152   Mean 38.5, Upper quartile 48 cm

The mean of grouped data is calculated as $\overline{x} = \dfrac{\Sigma fx}{\Sigma f}$ where x is the mid value.

So, firstly find the mid values:

cm	mid point (x)	f		fx
10 – 20	15	5	15×5 =	75
20 – 30	25	12	25×12 =	300
30 – 40	35	15	35×15 =	525
40 – 50	45	17	45×17 =	765
50 – 60	55	7	55×7 =	385
60 – 70	65	4	65×4 =	260
		$\Sigma f = 60$		Σfx = 2,310

$\overline{x} = \dfrac{\Sigma fx}{\Sigma f}$

$= \dfrac{2,310}{60} = 38.5$

Using the above data

Frequency	Cumulative frequency
5	5
12	17
15	32
17	49
7	56
4	60

The upper quartile is the value below which 75% of the population falls. This is therefore the $75\% \times 60 = 45^{th}$ item.

From the table above we can see that the 45th item falls in the 40 – 50 cm class. As there are 17 items in this class and the 45th item is the 13th item in this class, the value of the 45th item

$$= 40 + \left(\frac{13}{17} \times 10\right) = 40 + 7.647 = 47.647$$

≈ 48 cm (to the nearest cm)

153 £60,000

Firstly we need to find the cumulative frequency

Earnings £	No employed frequency	Cumulative frequency
20,000	6	6
30,000	6	12
60,000	10	22
70,000	2	24
80,000	4	28
110,000	3	31

The median is then found as the $\frac{n+1}{2}$ th item = $\frac{31+1}{2}$ th item = 16th item

From the table, this item has an annual earnings value of £60,000.

154 21.82

Firstly we need to find the cumulative frequency

Value of order (£)

At least	Less than	Frequency	Cumulative frequency
1	10	5	5
10	20	7	12
20	30	11	23
30	40	16	39
40	50	10	49
50	60	4	53
60	70	3	56

As the lower quartile is the value which 25% of the population falls below, it is the 25% × 56 = 14th item.

This item lies in the class at least 20 but less than 30.

There are 11 items in this class and the 14th item overall is the 2nd item in this class.

$$\text{The lower quartile (at least) 20} = 20 + \left[\frac{2}{11} \times (30 - 20)\right]$$

$$= 20 + 1.8182 = 21.8182$$

$$= 21.82 \text{ (to two decimal places)}$$

155 **A**

The median is the value of the middle item in the set.

Since there are an even number of values, this will be the $\dfrac{4^{th}\ value + 5^{th}\ value}{2}$

When $(17 + x)$ is greater than 11, the 4th and 5th values are 9 and 11, making the median = $\dfrac{9+11}{2} = 10$.

When $(17 + x)$ is less than 11, this value will affect the value of the 4th and 5th items.

Hence when $x = -7$, the numbers are 5, 6, 8, 9, 10, 11, 13, 14 and the median = $\dfrac{9+10}{2} = 9.5$

$\neq 10$.

(Note that this result can also be obtained by trial and error.)

156 **All except a questionnaire.**

Secondary data is data which has been collected for some other enquiry than the one of immediate interest, so *The Times*, a financial news website and CIMA *Insider* could all be classified as sources of secondary data.

157 **It eliminates selection bias.**

158 **A**

$$\text{Coefficient of variation} = \frac{\text{Standard deviation} \times 100}{\text{Arithmetic mean}}$$

159 $\dfrac{\textbf{Frequency}}{\textbf{3}}$

Remember that the area of each rectangle (rather than the height) represents the frequency of a particular class interval.

160 **£43.78**

Current price	= £65.67
Current index	= 150
Base index	= 100

$$\therefore \text{Price/kg in base year} = \frac{100}{150} \times £65.67$$

$$= 43.779995$$

$$= £43.78$$

161   Mean = 46.67, Median = 45.00, Mode = 56.00

$$\text{The mean} = \frac{33 + 45 + 39 + 56 + 44 + 36 + 50 + 61 + 56}{9}$$

$$= \frac{420}{9}$$

$$= 46.66666$$

$$= 46.67 \text{ (to two decimal places)}$$

The median is the middle number when the values are placed in order.

In order, the numbers are:

33   36   39   44   (45)   50   56   56   61

so the median   = 45

$$= 45.00 \text{ (to two decimal places)}$$

The mode is the most commonly occurring number. 56 occurs twice and all other numbers only occur once, so the answer is 56.00 (to two decimal places).

162   D

This is the definition of an ogive.

163   D

Let mid-point of estimate = a

Then £21.50   =   100% + 5% of mid-point

                =   1.05a

Re-arranging:

$$a = \frac{£21.50}{1.05} \quad = \quad £20.48 \text{ (to two decimal places)}$$

164   C

$$\frac{x - 850}{74.63} = \pm 0.67$$

Since we require the lower quartile score:

x   = $-(0.67 \times 74.63) + 850$

x   = $-50 + 850$

x   =   800

165   B

$$\text{Price/kg in base year} = \text{Current price} \times \frac{\text{Base year}}{\text{Current year}}$$

$$= £55.35 \times \frac{100}{135} = £41$$

166   B

$$1994\ \text{Index} \times \frac{1996\ \text{Index}}{100} \quad = \quad 126 \times \frac{109}{100}$$

$$= \quad 137.34$$

167   B

The median is the middle number when they are put in ascending numerical order.

Reordering: 0, 0, 1, 2, 3, 4, 4, 10

$\uparrow$

So, the median is between 2 & 3

The median is $\therefore \dfrac{2+3}{2} = 2.5$

168   C

$$\text{Mean} = \frac{\Sigma f}{n}$$

$$= \frac{0+0+1+2+3+4+4+10}{8}$$

$$= \frac{24}{8}$$

$$= 3$$

169   A

This is **stratified** as the population has been divided into several well defined groups (called strata).

PROBABILITY

170   B

The following information is given by the question:

(i)   There are 100 students in total.

(ii)   30 students are male (hence $100 - 30 = 70$ are female).

(iii)   55 students are studying for Certificate Stage (hence $100 - 55 = 45$ are not studying for Certificate Stage).

(iv)   6 male students are not studying (hence $30 - 6 = 24$ are studying).

For simplicity this information can be placed into a table.

	Not studying	Studying	Total
Male	6	$(30 - 6) = 24$	30
Female	$(45 - 6) = 39$	$(70 - 39) = 31$	70
Total	45	55	100

The probability that a randomly chosen female student is not studying is $\dfrac{39}{70}$,

ie P(NS/F) = 0.56.

171 A

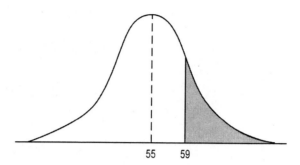

$$z = \frac{59-55}{\sqrt{14.44}} = 1.05$$

From tables, the probability of a score of 59 or more is $0.5 - 0.3531 \approx 0.15$

172 C

P (female (F))	= 0.6
P (CIMA (C))	= 0.8
P (F or C)	= P(F) + P(C) − P(F) P(C)
	= 0.6 + 0.8 − 0.48
	= 0.92

173 C

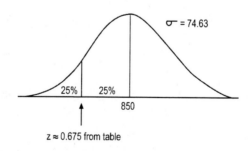

Lower quartile score = 850 - 0.675(74.63) $\cong$ 800

174 C

P (No sales) = P (No sale at A) × P (No sale at B)

= 0.7 × 0.7 = 0.49

175 A

P (No sale at first) × P (No sale at second) × P (Sale at third)

= 0.4 × 0.4 × 0.6

= 0.096

176   B

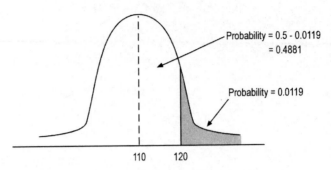

From normal distribution tables, a probability of 0.4881 corresponds to 2.26 standard deviations above the mean.

Therefore one standard deviation = $\dfrac{£10}{2.26}$ = 4.42 (to two decimal places)

177   C

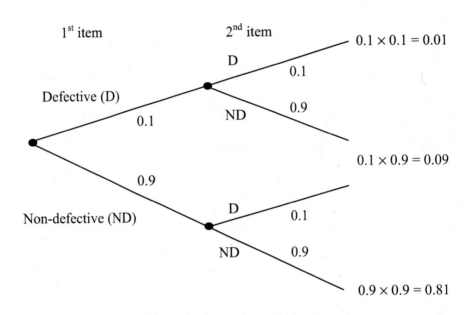

P (only one defective)   = P (1st defective, 2nd not) + P (1st not, 2nd defective)

= 0.09 + 0.09

= 0.18

178   C

P (day 1 = 25, day 2 = 35) = 0.4 × 0.6 = 0.24

P (day 1 = 35, day 2 = 25) = 0.6 × 0.4 = 0.24

P (either of these two possibilities) = 0.24 + 0.24 = 0.48

179 D

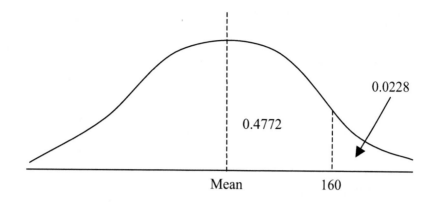

From tables, the z-score for 0.4772 is 2.0.

∴ 160 is 2 standard deviations above the mean

∴ Mean = 160 − (2 × 30) = 100.

180 D

P (Satellite or Video)   = P (Satellite) + P (Video) − P (Satellite and Video)

                         = 0.3 + 0.8 − (0.3 × 0.8) = 0.86

181 B

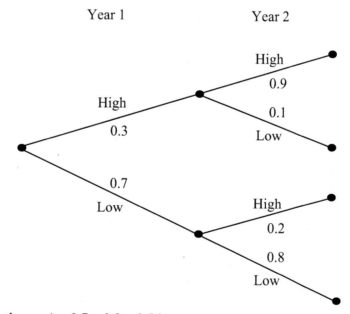

P (Low in both years) = 0.7 × 0.8 = 0.56

182 D

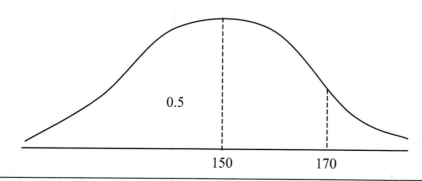

Mean = 150

$\sigma = \sqrt{100} = 10$

170 therefore lies $\dfrac{170-150}{10} = 2$ standard deviations above the mean

From tables, P (150 to 170) = 0.4772

$\therefore$ P (<170) = 0.5 + 0.4772 = 0.9772

183 D

Expected value by Expert W $= 0.2\times 1 + 0.3\times 0.5 + 0.5\times 0.25 = 0.475$
Expected value by Expert X $= 0.1\times 1 + 0.4\times 0.5 + 05\times 0.25 = 0.425$
Expected value by Expert Y $= 0.1\times 1 + 0.6\times 0.5 + 0.3\times 0.25 = 0.475$

Both W and Y have the highest expected sales.

184 B

P(at least one error detected) $= 1 - $ P(no errors detected)

$= 1 - (0.2 \times 0.3 \times 0.4)$

185 A

$0 \times 10 = 0$
$1 \times 5 = 5$
$2 \times 15 = 30$
$3 \times 15 = 45$
$4 \times 5 = 20$
_____
100
_____

Expected weekly demand = 100/50 = 2

186 D

$z = \dfrac{300-285}{10}$

z = 1.5

From tables = 0.4332

Percentage longer than 285 = 0.5 + 0.4332

= 0.9332

= 93%

187 B

From the data, if 60 invoices out of 200 have no errors, then 140 out of the 200 must have some error.

∴ The percentage *with* errors   is $\dfrac{140}{200} \times 100$

$$= 70\%$$

188 A

The expected value = the mean. We need to use the formula: mean = $\dfrac{\Sigma f}{n}$

From the data, $\Sigma f = (0 \times 60) + (1 \times 30) + (2 \times 40) + (3 \times 40) + (4 \times 20) + (5 \times 10) + (6 \times 0)$

$= 0 + 30 + 80 + 120 + 80 + 50 + 0$

$= 360$

From the data, n = 200

∴ mean $= \dfrac{360}{200}$

$= 1.8$

189 D

Using the formula

$Z = \dfrac{X - \mu}{\sigma}$

$Z = \dfrac{30 - 20}{5}$

$= 2$

From the tables, Z = 2 gives an area of 0.4772 between the mean (20) and the X value (30).

∴ The total area *below* X $= 0.5 + 0.4772$

$= 0.9772$ (or 97.72%)

190 D

P (an alarm fails) $= \dfrac{1}{100}$

∴ P (all 3 alarms fail ∴ security system fails) $= \dfrac{1}{100} \times \dfrac{1}{100} \times \dfrac{1}{100}$

$= \dfrac{1}{1{,}000{,}000}$

191 A

$$P(X/Y) = \frac{P(X \text{ and } Y)}{P(Y)}$$

$$\frac{1}{2} = \frac{P(X \text{ and } Y)}{\frac{1}{5}}$$

So $P(X \text{ and } Y) = \frac{1}{2} \times \frac{1}{5} = \frac{1}{10}$

$$P(Y/X) = \frac{P(Y \text{ and } X)}{P(X)}$$

$$= \frac{\frac{1}{10}}{\frac{2}{5}} = \frac{1}{10} \times \frac{5}{2} = \frac{1}{4}$$

192 B

P (under 25 and spent £50 to £200) $= \dfrac{125}{500} = 0.25$

193 D

P (spent £50 to £200, given under 25) $= \dfrac{125}{55+125+10} = 0.66$

194 C

P (under 25, given spent £50 to £200) $= \dfrac{125}{125+80} = 0.61$

195 B

Mean = 100 mm, standard deviation = 5 mm

Probability that length < 95 mm is probability that item is at least 1 standard deviation below mean.

From tables, area below $z = -1$ is $0.5 - 0.3413 = 15.87\%$

196 C

If the telephone call is answered for the first time on the fifth attempt then for the first four attempts it was not answered. The probability of it not being answered is 0.8 for four attempts followed by the probability of it being answered on the fifth attempt of 0.2.

Therefore probability is $(0.8)^4 \times (0.2)$

197 A

Probability $= 400/5{,}200$

$= 0.769$

$= 0.08$ (to two decimal places)

198 B

West buyers	= 1,300
Under 25s	= 1,600
West and under 25	= 400
West or under 25	= 1,300 + 1,600 − 400
	= 2,500
Probability	= 2,500/5,200
	= 0.48

199 C

Probability = 600/1,600

= 0.375

200 A

Probability = 1,600/5,200 × 1,599/ 5,199

= 0.0946 = 0.09 (to two decimal places)

201 B

In a single throw of two dice, there are 6×6 possible combinations of the faces, therefore 36 combinations. A total score of 7 can be obtained by:

1+6, 2+5,3+4,4+3,5+2,6+1, ie in six ways.

So the probability that a result is two numbers which sum up to seven is $\dfrac{6}{36}$ or $\dfrac{1}{6}$

202 C

$$P (A \text{ or } E) = P (A) + P(E) - P (A \text{ and } E)$$

$$= \frac{1}{4}+\frac{1}{3}-\left(\frac{1}{4}\times\frac{1}{3}\right) = \frac{6}{12}$$

$$= \frac{1}{2}$$

203 B

The probability that none are faulty is the same as the probability that all 10 are fine,

ie $0.9 \times 0.9 \times 0.9 \times 0.9 \times 0.9 \times 0.9 \times 0.9 \times 0.9 \times 0.9 \times 0.9$ (or 0.9^{10})

= 0.348678

or 34.8678%

≈ 35%

204 A

There are two ways of tackling this question.

1   The chances of selecting a loser would be picking a red, green or brown ball.

$$= 0.4 + 0.3 + 0.2 = 0.9$$

or

2   Chances of selecting winning ball

$$= 0.1$$

so losing ball = 1 - 0.1 = 0.9

205 D

Forget about football for a second and think about the possible outcomes.

Match 1 - possible outcomes = City win, United win, draw

Match 2 - possible outcomes = City win, United win, draw

So City have 1 in 3 chance of winning a match.

To win both matches odds are $\dfrac{1}{3} \times \dfrac{1}{3}$ = 1 in 9

206 C

$$Z = \frac{x - \mu}{\sigma}$$

$$Z = \frac{x - 200}{\sqrt{36}}$$

From tables*:

$$0.67 = \frac{x - 200}{6}$$

$$4.02 = x - 200$$

$$x = 204.02$$

The lower quartile is therefore:

$$200 - 4.02 = 195.98 \approx 196$$

* The lower quartile is below where 25% of the score fall. The value of 0.67 is found from the 'area under the normal curve' table provided.

207 C

Probabilities

Male = 40, $\therefore$ female = 60

Spend £10 or more = 70, $\therefore$ spend less than £10 = 30

Then P(female or < £10) = P(female and < £10) + P(male and < £10) + P(female and > £10)

$$= (0.6 \times 0.3) + (0.4 \times 0.3) + (0.6 \times 0.7) = 0.72$$

208 **D**

Using the formula $Z = \dfrac{x - \mu}{\sigma}$

$Z = \dfrac{175 - 150}{40}$

$= 0.63$

From the tables, the corresponding area for deviations

$= 0.2357$

This means that the proportion of the population below 175 units

$= 0.5 + 0.2357$

$= 0.7357 = 73.57\%$

Therefore the closest answer is 74%

209 **89.50%**

Firstly, write down all the information that you know.

Male $= 35$ $\therefore$ female $= 100 - 35 = 65$

Studying law $= 70$, $\therefore$ not $= 100 - 70 = 30$

You can now calculate the probability.

P (female or studying law)

$=$ P (female + studying law) + P (female + not studying law) + P (male and studying law)

$= (0.65 \times 0.70) + (0.65 \times 0.30) + (0.35 \times 0.70)$

$= 0.455 + 0.195 + 0.245$

$= 0.895$

The probability that a student chosen at random is either female or studying law is 89.50%.

210 **Project Y, EV = £3,500**

To decide which project to go for, you need to work out which one will generate the most profit (expected value), so the question is slightly misleading in that it asks which to choose and then the expected value!

Expected value

Project X $\quad = (0.4 \times £3,000) + (0.6 \times £1,500)$

$= 1,200 + 900$

$= £2,100$

Project Y $\quad = (0.35 \times £10,000) + (0.65 \times 0)$

$= 3,500 + 0$

$= £3,500$

So, project Y has a higher expected value of profit which means it could offer a better return than X. Hence, project Y should be chosen.

The expected value of profit $= £3,500$.

211   C

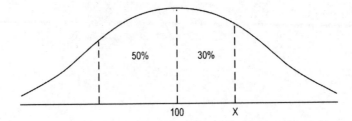

To answer this, you need to find the point above the mean where 80% of the frequencies are below and 20% are above it.

In other words, where 50 – 20 = 30% of frequencies are between Z and the mean.

Using normal distribution tables, 30% of frequencies are between the mean and a point 0.84 standard deviations from the mean.

So, using the formula

$$Z = \frac{x - \mu}{\sigma}$$

$$0.84 = \frac{x - 100}{20}$$

$$16.8 = x - 100$$

$$x = 100 + 16.8$$

$$= 116.8$$

$$\approx 117 \text{ to the nearest whole number}$$

212   0.06

P (exactly 4 heads) $= 0.5 \times 0.5 \times 0.5 \times 0.5$

$= 0.0625$

≈ 0.06 to 2 decimal places.

213   2.28%

Using:

$$Z = \frac{x - \mu}{\sigma}$$

$$= \frac{190 - 200}{5}$$

$$= -2$$

From the tables, a z value of 2 corresponds to a probability of 0.4772.

This value is the value of the area between the mean and z, ie:

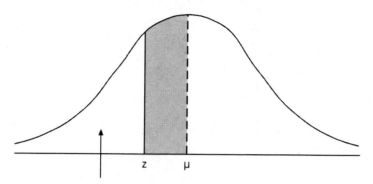

and we need the area below z,

ie $0.5 - 0.4772 = 0.0228$

∴ The percentage less than 190 cm is 2.28%.

214   All three are.

The normal distribution is symmetrical and bell-shaped.

The area under the curve is one unit of area.

The mean, median and mode lie together in the axis of the symmetry of the curve.

215   0.21

If 2 light bulbs are chosen at random

P(only one defective)   =   P (1st defective) × P (2nd not defective) +
                                    P (1st not defective) × P(2nd defective)

= $(0.12 \times 0.88) + (0.88 \times 0.12)$

= $0.1056 + 0.1056$

= 0.2112

≈   0.21 to 2 decimal places.

216   0.38

Probability of sale at A   = 0.25 so no sale = 0.75

Probability of sale at B   = 0.5   so no sale = 0.5

P (no sale)   = P (no sale at A) × P (no sale at B)

= 0.75×0.5

= 0.375

≈ 0.38 to 2 decimal places.

217   0.9977

$\mu = 110$

$\sigma^2 = 50$

∴ $\sigma = 7.0710678$

Using:

$$Z = \frac{x - \mu}{\sigma}$$

$$= \frac{130 - 110}{7.0710678}$$

$$= 2.8284271$$

Using tables, a Z value of 2.83 corresponds to a probability of 0.4977.

Therefore, the probability that sales are less than 130 in any week $\quad = 0.5 + 0.4977$

$$= 0.9977$$

218 0.55

P (female) = 0.6 $\qquad \therefore$ P (male not female) = 0.4

P (blue eyes) = 0.25 $\qquad \therefore$ P (not blue eyes) = 0.75

P (male or has blue eyes) = P (male) + P (blue eyes) – P (male + blue eyes)

$$= 0.4 + 0.25 - (0.4 \times 0.25)$$

$$= 0.65 - 0.1$$

$$= 0.55$$

219 0.24, 0.55

Looking at the table, the number of under 18s spending £20 – £40 is 60.

There are a total of 250 customers.

$\therefore$ the probability a customer is under 18 and spent £20 – £40 $\quad = \dfrac{60}{250}$

$$= 0.24$$

Think carefully about this second part. 'If a customer is under 18' means we *only* need to look at the sample under 18, ie 110 people.

$\therefore$ the probability an under 18 year old spends £20 – £40 $\quad = \dfrac{60}{110}$

$$= 0.5454545$$

$$\approx 0.55 \text{ to 2 decimal places}$$

220 43.56%

60% = woman

15% = economics

P (woman or economics) = P (woman) + P (economics) – P (woman + economics)

$$= 0.6 + 0.15 - (0.6 \times 0.15)$$

$$= 0.75 - 0.09$$

$$= 0.66$$

Since there are *two* students, the probability $= 0.66 \times 0.66$

$$= 0.4356$$

To 2 decimal places = 43.56%.

221   **0.31**

Remember there are 4 suits in a pack of cards, each consisting of 13 cards.

P(King) $= \dfrac{4}{52}$

$= 0.076923$

$= 0.08$

P(Spade) $= \dfrac{13}{52}$

$= 0.25$

P(King of spades) $= \dfrac{1}{52}$

$= 0.0192307$

≈ 0.02

P(King or spade) $= P(King) + P(Spade) - P(King of spades)$

$= \dfrac{4}{52} + \dfrac{13}{52} - \dfrac{1}{52}$

$= \dfrac{16}{52}$

$= 0.3076923$

≈ 0.31

222   Probability X > 120 = **2 + 3 + 4**

Probability X < 120 = **1**

Probability X < 160 = **1 + 2 + 3**

223   **18.41%**

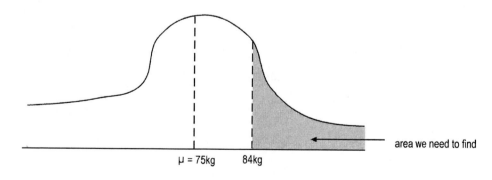

Using Z $= \dfrac{x - \mu}{\sigma}$

$= \dfrac{84 - 75}{10}$

$= 0.9$

From tables, this Z value corresponds to a probability of 0.3159. This is the proportion of balls that weigh between 75 kg and 84 kg.

So, the % of balls weighing more than 84 kg

$$= \quad (0.5 - 0.3159) \times 100$$

$$= \quad 18.41 \text{ (to 2 decimal places)}$$

224 D

Here it is easier to calculate the opposite.

Someone who is neither male nor employed is a female who is unemployed.

Probability of being female =	0.4	
Probability of being unemployed =	0.3	
Probability of being female and unemployed =	0.4×0.3	$= 0.12$
So, probability of being male or employed =	$1 - 0.12$	$= 0.88$

225 A

60 large, 40 small companies (ie 100 total)

40 large companies are slow payers

∴ 20 large companies are fast payers

But total of 30 companies are fast payers

∴ 10 small companies are fast payers

Then fast paying small company $= \dfrac{10}{100} = 0.10$

226 B

For a 99% confidence internal:

Z	=	$+2.575$
Z	=	$\dfrac{x - \mu}{\sigma}$
2.575	=	$\dfrac{95.8 - \mu}{16.2}$
41.715	=	$95.8 - \mu$
μ	=	54.085, to the nearest whole number equals 54

227 B

Firstly, we need to find the sales mid-points and the probability (frequency) of each.

Sales mid-   Probability

points	
5	0.05
15	0.20
25	0.60
35	0.10
45	0.05

Then we need to multiply sales by probability and add the answers together.

Expected value   = $(5 \times 0.05) + (15 \times 0.2) + (25 \times 0.6) + (35 \times 0.1) + (45 \times 0.05)$

=   24

228   A

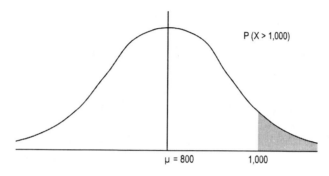

We need to calculate the shaded area.

Using Z = $\dfrac{x - \mu}{\sigma}$

Z = $\dfrac{x - 800}{200}$

For overtime cost exceeding £1,000 (ie x > £1,000), Z > 1

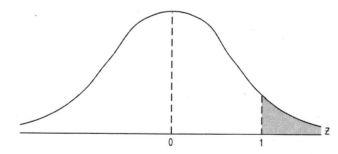

Then   P (Z > 1)   = 0.5 − 0.3413 (from tables)

= 0.1587

---

229 C

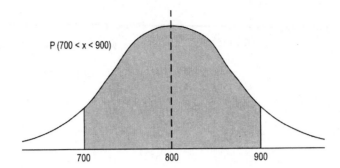

$$Z = \frac{x - 800}{200}$$

For overtime cost between £700 and £900 (ie 700 < x < 900), −0.5 < Z < 0.5

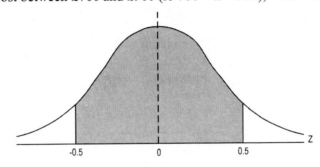

Then P (− 0.5 < Z < 0.5) = 2 × 0.1915 (from tables)

$$= 0.3830$$

230 C

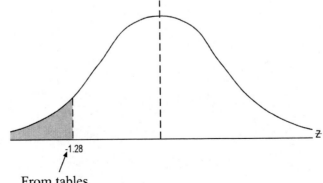

$$Z = \frac{x - 800}{200}$$

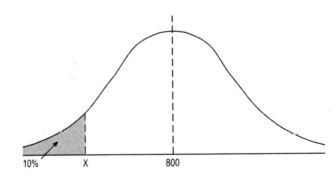

From tables

Therefore (−1.28 × 200) + 800 = x

ie x $= 800 - 256$

                       $= 544$

231   B

P (both A and B work)

= $P(A) \times P(B)$

= 0.9×0.8

= 0.72

232   A

P (both don't work)

= $[1 - P(A \text{ works})] \times [1 - P(B \text{ works})]$

= $(1 - 0.9)(1 - 0.8)$

= 0.1×0.2

= 0.02

233   D

P (only one works)

= $P(A \text{ works, B doesn't}) + P(B \text{ works, A doesn't})$

= $(0.9 \times 0.2) + (0.8 \times 0.1)$

= $0.18 + 0.08$

= 0.26

234   C

P (at least one will work)

= $P(A + B \text{ work}) + P(\text{only 1 works})$

= $0.72 + 0.26$

= 0.98

FINANCIAL MATHEMATICS

235   C

As interest is calculated on a quarterly basis, the annual percentage rate must first be calculated.

$$APR = (1 + \frac{i}{t})^t - 1$$

where   i   is the nominal interest rate of 8%

t   is the number of periods over a year in which the interest is calculated (ie 4 times a year (quarterly))

Inserting the figures into the formula above gives:

$$
\begin{aligned}
APR &= (1 + \frac{0.08}{4})^4 - 1 \\
&= (1.02)^4 - 1 \\
&= 1.08243 - 1 \\
&= 8.243\%
\end{aligned}
$$

Once the APR has been calculated, this can be inserted into the general formula for compound interest:

$$= P(1 + i)^t$$

where P is the original sum invested

i is the interest rate

t is the total number of years

The question gives:

$$P = 12,000$$

$$i = 0.08243$$

$$t = 3$$

Then compound interest $= 12,000\,(1 + 0.08243)^3$

$$= 15,218.9$$

$$= £15,219$$

236   D

Turn to the 'cumulative present value of £1' table in the mathematical tables provided. This shows the present value of £1 per annum receivable at the **end** of each year for n years ahead. Our farmer is receiving £500 now (present value = £500), plus further payments of £500 at the **end** of each of the next five years. The present value of this amount, at 7%, is found by looking in the tables in the 7% column, year 5 row. The factor is 4.100, leading to a present value of £500 × 4.100 = £2,050. This must be added to the £500 receivable now, to give a total of £2,550.

237   C

The cost after one year is £10,000 × 0.95; after two years is £10,000 × 0.95 × 0.95; after three years is £10,000 × 0.95^3; and after four years is £10,000 × 0.95^4. But $0.95^4 = 0.8145$. Therefore the cost after four years is £10,000 × 0.8145 = £8,145.

238   B

Let A = annuity. Then:

£60,000 = A × 5-year annuity factor at 5% (4.329 from tables)

Thus A = 60,000/4.329 = £13,860

239   C

Each year the costs fall to (100 − 2.5)% = 97.5% of its previous total

After five years the costs will be £160,000$(0.975)^5$ = £140,975

240   D

$$\frac{5,319.60}{1,200} = 4.433$$

⇒   Payable from time 0 to time n. Factor at time 0 is 1.

⇒   Annuity factor is 4.433 − 1 = 3.433. From tables 3.433 is the annuity factor @ 14% for five years.

The lease is for five years plus the payment now, ie 6 years in total.

241   B

Annual rate is 6%.

Approximate monthly rate is 0.5%.

⇒ $1,000 \times (1.005)^6 = 1,030.38$

Then interest = £1,030.38 − £1,000 = £30.38

242   D

£x × annuity factor for 7 years at 8% (= 5.206 from tables) = £33,995.18

⇒   £x = $\dfrac{33,995.18}{5.206}$ = £6,530

243   B

£1,360 × af = 6,101

⇒   af = $\dfrac{6,101}{1,360}$ = 4.486 ⇒ from tables rate is 9%

244 **C**

Let the annual equal payments be for £x.

Then £x × annuity factor for years 1 to 4 at 8% = £26,496

ie £x = $\dfrac{£26,496}{3.312}$ = £8,000

Total amount paid = £10,000 + (4 × £8,000)

= £42,000

245 **C**

This is the definition of net present value.

246 **C**

The Mathematical Tables include the formula for the present value of an annuity of £1:

PV = $\dfrac{1}{r} - \dfrac{1}{r(1+r)^t}$

Try r = 8%

PV = $\left(\dfrac{1}{0.08} - \dfrac{1}{0.08(1.08)^{10}} \right) \times £5,000$

= (12.5 − 5.79) × £5,000

= £33,550

So 8% is the correct interest rate.

247 **B**

$$1,494.87 \left[\frac{1}{1.07} + - - - - - + \left(\frac{1}{1.07} \right)^{10} \right]$$

$$= \frac{1,494.87}{1.07} \left[\frac{\left(\frac{1}{1.07} \right)^{10} - 1}{\frac{1}{1.07} - 1} \right]$$

$$= 1,397.07 \left[\frac{-0.49165}{-0.06542} \right]$$

= £10,500

Alternatively, using annuity tables:

1,494.87 × annuity factor for 10 years at 7%

= 1,494.87 × 7.024

= £10,500

248 C

Let the annual rental = r.

The rent is paid at the beginning of the year so this is equivalent to paying at the end of the previous year. So, year 1 payment has a discount factor of 1 (ie year 0) and years 2 to 5 payments have a discount factor of 3.17 (ie cumulative present value for 4 years at 10%)

$(r \times 1) + (r \times 3.17)$ = £32,800

4.17r   = £32,800

r   = £7,866

249 D

$$\frac{£8,000}{0.07} = £114,286$$

250 A

NPV = (£6,500 × Annuity factor) – £25,000

= (£6,500 × 4.486) – £25,000

= £4,159

251 C

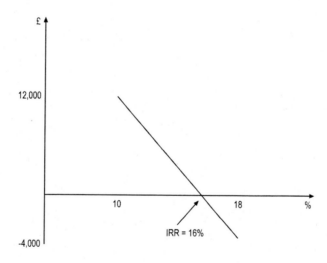

252 D

From formulae for perpetuity $PV = \dfrac{1}{r}$ (for £1) where r = % interest

∴ for £15,000, PV = $\dfrac{£15,000}{0.09}$

= £166,666.67

253   B

Using the cumulative present value tables, of £1

For n = 15 and r = 6% we have 9.712

Then for £200,000, annual repayment is £R = $\dfrac{£200,000}{9.712}$ = £20,593

254   C

Interest payable on year 3, in 3 years' time is £3,000 × 10% = £300.

The PV of this £300 = $\dfrac{£300}{(1.1)^3}$ or $\dfrac{£300}{\left(\frac{11}{10}\right)^3}$

Rearranging the equation:

$\dfrac{£300}{\left(\frac{11}{10}\right)^3} = £300 \times \dfrac{10^3}{11^3}$

$= £300 \times \left(\dfrac{10}{11}\right)^3$

255   A

The present value of £1 today = £1; this represents the 1st payment.

There are then 9 more payments to follow (occurring in 1-9 years' time). The cumulative PV of 9 years @ 12%, read from the tables, is 5.328, add this to the Present Value (PV) of 1;

5.328+1.000 = 6.328

The present value of the lease is £8,000 × 6.328 = £50,624

256   C

$\dfrac{12}{1.01}$ = 1.126825

257   D

$\dfrac{£10,000}{0.08}$ = £125,000

258   C

From mathematical tables, the annuity factor for 8% over ten years = 6.710.

Value of annuity ∴   = 6.710 × £8,000

= £53,680

PV of £53,680 at the end of 3 years at 8%

= £53,680 × 0.794 (from tables)

= £42,622

259   B

£80,000 × $(1 - 0.08)^6$

= £48,508.40

≈ £48,508

260   A

Annuity factor from tables is 6.145

£1,000 × 6.145

Annuity = £6,145

Discounted for three years (from present value tables)

0.751 × £6,145

= £4,614.895

≈ £4,615

261   D

There are two methods we can use to calculate this sum.

Method 1

Year	Opening balance	Interest	Closing balance
1	100	10% of 100	110
2	110	10% of 110	121
3	121	10% of 121	133.10

Method 2

V $= x(1 + r)^n$ where

   V = value

   x = original sum

   r = rate of interest

   n = time period

So V $= 100 \dfrac{(1+10)^3}{100}$

   $= 100 (1.1)^3$

   = £133.10 as before

262   £500,000

The present value of a perpetuity (from tables) is:

PV $= \dfrac{x}{r}$

Where   x = the annuity (£30,000)

   r = interest rate per annum (6%)

PV $= \dfrac{30,000}{0.06}$

   = £500,000

---

263   True

If the asset's value depreciates at 12% per annum, it is worth 88% of its start-of-year value at the end of each year.

$\therefore$ £500,000 $\times (0.88)^6$

$= 500,000 \times 0.464404$

$= £232,202$

This is to the nearest £ so the statement is TRUE.

264   False

A perpetuity is an annuity which lasts **forever**.

265   £5,706

$$\text{PV} \quad = \frac{1}{r}\left[1 - \frac{1}{(1+r)^n}\right]$$

$$£42,000 \quad = £X \times \left(\frac{1}{(0.06)}\right)\left(1 - \frac{1}{(1+0.06)^{10}}\right)$$

$$= £X \times 16.66 \times 0.441605$$

$$£X \quad = \frac{£42,000}{7.360087}$$

$$= £5,706.454$$

$$\approx £5,706$$

266   C

Increase from 1997 to 1999

$= \quad 140 - 115$

$= \quad 25$

As a percentage, increase

$= \quad \dfrac{25}{115} \times 100$

$= \quad 21.73$

$\approx \quad 21.7$

267   D

Rebased price for 2000

$= \quad \dfrac{152}{127} \times 100\%$

$= \quad 119.685$

$\approx \quad 119.7$

268 **B**

Using the formula $S = x (1 + r)^n$

We have:

S $=$ $2,000 (1 + 0.05)^5$

$=$ £2,552.56

$\approx$ £2,553

269 **D**

Double the value	$= £4,000$
£4,000	$= 2,000 (1 + 0.05)^n$
$\dfrac{4,000}{2,000}$	$= (1.05)^n$
2	$= (1.05)^n$
log 2	$= n \log 1.05$
n	$= \dfrac{\log 2}{\log 1.05}$
	$= \dfrac{0.30103}{0.0211892}$
	$= 14.206699$
	≈ 14.21

270 **A**

Using CIMA tables the discount factor for 6 years @ 6% = 0.705.

Present value

$=$ £15,000 × 0.705

$=$ £10,575

271 **A**

Using S $= x (1 + r)^n$, we have:

$= 1 (1 + 0.015)^{12}$

$= 1.1956182$

As a percentage this $\approx 19.56\%$

FORECASTING

272   B

The formula to calculate the coefficient of correlation is given as:

$$r = \frac{n\sum xy - (\sum x)(\sum y)}{\sqrt{(n\sum x^2 - (\sum x)^2)(n\sum y^2 - (\sum y)^2)}}$$

All values required for this formula are given within the question.

$\sum x$ = 440
$\sum y$ = 330
$\sum x^2$ = 17,986
$\sum y^2$ = 10,366
$\sum xy$ = 13,467
n = 11

These values need only be inserted into the formula, hence:

$$r = \frac{(11\times13,467)-(440\times330)}{\sqrt{((11\times17,986)-(440)^2)((11\times10,366)-(330)^2)}}$$

$$= \frac{148,137-145,200}{\sqrt{4,246\times5,126}}$$

$$= \frac{148,137-145,200}{4,665.297}$$

$$= 0.629$$

$$= 0.63$$

273   B

Trend   = y = 23.87 + 2.4x

Trend   = 23.87 + 2.4 (21) = 74.27

Forecast   = trend × seasonal variation

⇒ Forecast = 74.27 × 1.08 = 80.21

274   D

Seasonally adjusted actual figure $= \frac{2,200}{0.97} = 2,268$

275   D

y   = 9.72 + 5.816x

When x   = 23 and the monthly deviation is + 6.5, the forecast number of items sold is

y   = 9.72 + (5.816 × 23) + 6.5
           = 9.72 + 133.77 + 6.5
           = 149.99

276 D

If b = 0 the model would look like chart C, if b > 0 it would look like chart B and if b < 0 it would look like chart A.

277 D

Over a whole year (4 quarters), the seasonal variations must add up to 4.

$4 - (1.2 + 1.3 + 0.4) = 1.1$

278 A

Trend in quarter 1 $= \dfrac{125,000}{1.2} = £104,167$

Trend in quarter 2 $= \dfrac{130,000}{1.3} = £100,000$

∴ the trend has decreased from quarter 1 to quarter 2.

279 A

Correlation coefficient must lie between 1 and –1.

Slope of regression line can be any finite number.

Variance is always positive.

Statement (ii) only is true.

280 B

Perfect negative correlation.

281 D

£21.50 = mid point +5%, ie 1.05 mid point

mid point = £21.50/1.05 = £20.48

282 B

There is strong correlation between tasting good and looking good.

283 C

Perfect negative correlation, ie $R = -1 = 1 - \dfrac{6\Sigma d^2}{N(N^2 - 1)}$

Rearranging and substituting N = 10 gives $\dfrac{6\Sigma d^2}{10 \times 99} = 2$

ie $6\Sigma d^2 = 2 \times 10 \times 99$

$\Sigma d^2 = 330$

284 D

Costs = 1,500 + (15 × outputs)

Fixed costs = £1,500

Variable costs = £15

If output is 500 units, costs = 1,500 + 15 × 500 = 9,000

All 3 statements are true.

285 D

r = 0.9 indicates high positive correlation

R = 0.81, ie 81% of variation in weekly costs is attributable to amount produced.

Forecast using the regression equation should be reliable.

All 3 statements are incorrect.

286 C

$$\text{Trend} = \frac{1,600}{0.8}$$

$$= 2,000$$

287 A

Seasonal variation = 100% − 20% − 30%

= 50%

Total must be zero, ∴ seasonal variation for Q_4 is −50%

288 D

Logically, if law is perfectly negatively correlated with both FBSM and Accounting, then it follows that Accounting and FBSM must be perfectly positively correlated.

289 A

The slope of the line is −1 and cuts the Y axis at approximately X = 8

∴   the line is

Y   =   8 + (X × (−1))

=   8 − X

290 B

Trend   = 483.45 − (1.65×13)

= 462

Forecast   = trend + seasonal factor

= 462 + 21.45

= 483.45

≈ 483

---

291 **True**

292 **−0.86**

Using the formula

$$r = \frac{n\Sigma xy - \Sigma x\Sigma y}{\sqrt{[n\Sigma x^2 - (\Sigma x)^2][n\Sigma y^2 - (\Sigma y)^2]}}$$

$$= \frac{(12\times124,258) - (802\times1,850)}{\sqrt{[(12\times53,792) - 802^2][(12\times287,868) - 1,850^2]}}$$

$$= \frac{1,491,096 - 1,483,700}{\sqrt{2,300\times31,916}}$$

$$= \frac{-7,396}{8,567.777}$$

$$= -0.863234$$

$$\approx -0.86 \text{ (to 2 decimal points).}$$

293 **Two variables show a high degree of correlation but have no direct correlation.**

294 **The slope of the equation if plotted on a graph is 3 and the line cuts the axis at 4 if plotted on a graph.**

295 **y = 1.8 + 2.2x**

x	y	x^2	xy
2	6	4	12
3	8	9	24
4	12	16	48
5	12	25	60
14	38	54	144

$$n = 4$$

$$\text{Using } b = \frac{n\Sigma xy - \Sigma x\Sigma y}{n\Sigma x^2 - (\Sigma x)^2}$$

$$= \frac{(4\times144) - (14\times38)}{4\times54 - 14^2}$$

$$= \frac{44}{20}$$

$$= 2.2$$

$$a \quad = \quad \bar{y} - b\bar{x}$$

$$= \quad \frac{38}{4} - (2.2 \times \frac{14}{4})$$

$$= \quad 9.5 - 7.7$$

$$= \quad 1.8$$

$$\therefore y \quad = \quad 1.8 + 2.2x$$

296 True

297 All three are true

298 B

The actual times series values are shown on the bottom line of a Z chart.

299 A

For year 1996, trend	=	$(0.0004 \times 1996^2) + (0.2 \times 1996) + 80.2$	= 2,073.0064
So forecast	=	$1.87 \times 2,073.0064$	= 3,876.522
Hence forecast	$\approx$	3,877	

300 B

Week	Sales £000	4-point moving average	4-point centred moving average
1	200		
2	240		
		227.5	
3	250		231.25
		235	
4	220		237.50
		240	
5	230		
6	260		

Hence second 4-point centred moving average = 237.50

301 A

If estimated total cost = £12 (± 1), the product could cost £11 to £13.

If estimated selling price = £20 (± £3), product could sell at £17 to £23.

Profit could ∴ vary	from	£17 − £13 = £4
	to	£23 − £11 = £12

So, the estimated profit per unit will be £8 (± £4).

302 A

From formulae, correlation coefficient equation is

$$r = \frac{n\sum XY - \sum X \sum Y}{\sqrt{(n\sum X^2 - (\sum X)^2)(n\sum Y^2 - (\sum Y)^2)}}$$

$$= \frac{(6\times 7) - (1\times 15)}{\sqrt{((6\times 15) - (1)^2)((6\times 65) - (15)^2)}}$$

$$= \frac{42 - 15}{\sqrt{(90 - 1)(390 - 225)}}$$

$$= \frac{27}{\sqrt{14,685}}$$

$$= \frac{27}{121.1817}$$

$$= 0.222806$$

$$\approx 0.22$$

Section 4

ANSWERS TO PRACTICE QUESTIONS

BASIC MATHEMATICS

1   ENGINEERING ASSETS

Tutorial note

To construct a component bar chart, calculate the total value for each year and then sub-divide for the five component assets.

To construct a percentage component bar chart, we need to calculate the value of each of the assets as a percentage of the total.

Calculating the percentage increase in assets over 5 years is a give away for 6 marks.

(a)

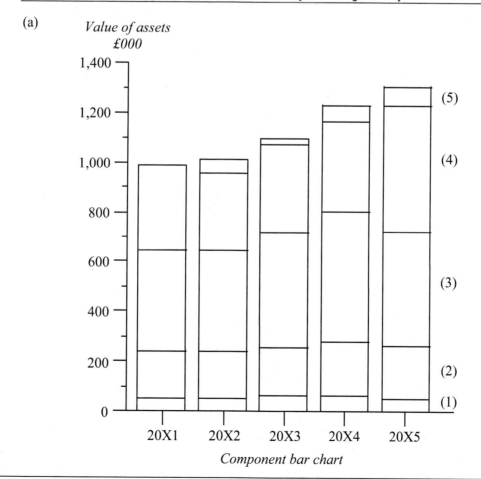

Component bar chart

Assets ordered as:

(1)   Property

(2)   Plant and machinery

(3)   Stock and work in progress

(4)   Debtors

(5)   Cash

To construct a percentage component bar chart, we need to calculate the value of each of the assets as a percentage of the total, as follows:

Asset	20X1		20X2		20X3		20X4		20X5	
	£000	%	£000	%	£000	%	£000	%	£000	%
Property	59	6.0	59	5.8	65	5.8	70	5.6	74	5.7
Plant & machinery	176	17.9	179	17.5	195	17.4	210	16.9	200	15.3
Stock and WIP	409	41.7	409	40.1	448	39.9	516	41.5	479	36.7
Debtors	330	33.6	313	30.7	384	34.3	374	30.1	479	36.7
Cash	7	0.8	60	5.9	29	2.6	74	5.9	74	5.6
	981		1,020		1,121		1,244		1,306	

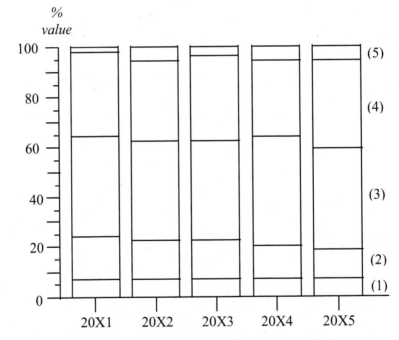

Percentage component bar chart

(b)   The total value of assets in 20X1 is **£981,000**.

The total value of assets in 20X5 is **£1,306,000**.

This represents an increase in the five-year period of £325,000. The percentage increase in the total value of assets

$$= \frac{325,000}{981,000} \times 100 = \textbf{33.1\%}$$

2   PROPORTIONAL REPRESENTATION

Tutorial note:

This question is a gentle introduction to business mathematics and is concerned with proportions and ratios. The key to answering these types of questions is to find the lowest common denominator and, if possible, to simplify the answer even further.

(a)   LCD = 50 pence   so $\dfrac{30}{51}$

can divide each side by 3   so $\dfrac{10}{17}$

or   **10:17**

(b)   If expenditure   = £4,500

and earnings   = £6,000

then savings   = £1,500

Ratio is 1,500:6,000   = **1:4** *Divide each side by 1,500*

(c)   Tax to gross income   = £1,450:£8,700

We are fortunate here that £8,700 divides by £1,450, so:

= **1:6**

(d)   (i)   When new   £4,500:£5,500

LCD = £500   so   = **9:11**

(ii)   Secondhand £3,250:£4,000

LCD = £250   so   = **13:16**

(e)   Ratio is £95:£1,425

Figures will divide by £95,   so   = **1:15**

(f)   Ratio is £7,950:£6,916.50

There is no LCD that springs to mind here. However, ratio is:

$1:\dfrac{£6,916.50}{£7,950}$ = **1:0.87**

(g)   Ratio 32:256

Divides by lower amount,   so   = **1:8**

(h)   Cash available to debts payable:

=   £3,400:£28,900

= $1:\dfrac{£28,900}{£3,400}$ so   = **1:8.5**

3 SCHOOL COSTS

Tutorial note:

There is no hidden agenda in a question like this and the calculations are quite easy. Do not get too complacent and write everything out in full.

(a) (i) The maximum absolute error   = **50p**

because £9.50 would be rounded up to £10 and £9.49 would be rounded down to £9.

(ii) The maximum relative error

$$= \frac{\text{Maximum absolute error}}{\text{Expected value}} \times 100\%$$

$$= \frac{£0.50}{£10} \times 100 = \textbf{5\%}$$

(iii) **The maximum absolute error is the largest value that the actual cost could differ from the expected value.**

The maximum relative error is expressed as a percentage and is the maximum absolute error expressed as a percentage of the expected value.

(b) (i)

Maximum cost of school uniform	= £50 + 5%	= **£52.50**
Maximum cost of school bus	= £20 + 4%	= **£20.80**
Maximum cost of school dance	= £15 + 3%	= **£15.45**
Minimum cost of school uniform	= £50 – 5%	= **£47.50**
Maximum cost of school uniform	= £20 – 4%	= **£19.20**
Maximum cost of school uniform	= £15 – 3%	= **£14.55**

(ii)

Maximum total expenditure	= £52.50 + £20.80 + £15.45	= **£88.75**
Minimum total expenditure	= £47.50 + £19.20 + £14.55	= **£81.25**

4 CALENDARS

Tutorial note:

Part (a) is quite straightforward. It is simply a case of adding up the relevant cost.

Part (b) involves being able to distinguish between fixed and variable costs in order to create a formula.

Part (c) requires the solution of a linear equation and then substituting specific total cost figures into the formula.

(a) Materials cost £0.50 per calendar.

(i) So natural cost   =   0.50N

Labour costs £10 per hour and N Calendars take $(\frac{N}{250} + 2$ hrs$)$

So labour costs   = $10(\frac{N}{250} + 2)$

                                = $\frac{N}{25} + 20$

(ii)	Distribution cost	=	£50 per hundred + £25
		=	$50 \times \dfrac{N}{100} + 25$
		=	$\dfrac{N}{2} + 25$
(iii)	Total cost	=	$0.50N + \dfrac{N}{25} + 20 + \dfrac{N}{2} + 25$
	Total cost	=	$1.04N + 45$
	Cost of producing 500 units	=	$1.04 \times 500 + 45$
		=	**£565**
(b)	Fixed cost	=	£45
	Variable cost	=	£1.04 per calendar
	Total cost	=	Fixed cost + Variable cost
	So formula	=	**£45 + £1.04N**
(c)	If cost = £1,000 then £1,000	=	£1.04N + £45
	$\therefore$ £955	=	£1.04N
	Thus $N = \dfrac{955}{1.04}$	=	**918 calendars**

5   SIMULTANEOUS LINEAR EQUATIONS

Tutorial note:

The key to solving simultaneous equations is to multiply both sides of the equation so that we have an x term or a y term that is the same. This can then be eliminated from the equation so that we only have one unknown variable.

(a)	$3x + 4y$	=	29	(i)
	$5x + 2y$	=	25	(ii)

Multiply equation (ii) by 2

We have	$10x + 4y$	=	50	(iii)
and	$3x + 4y$	=	29	(i)
	$\Rightarrow 7x$	=	21	
	$\Rightarrow \mathbf{x}$	=	**3**	
If x = 3,	$9 + 4y$	=	29	
	$4y$	=	20	
	$\mathbf{y}$	=	**5**	

(b)

$$6x + 7y = 33 \quad \text{(i)}$$
$$7x + 6y = 32 \quad \text{(ii)}$$

Multiply equation (i) by 7

Multiply equation (ii) by 6

We have
$$42x + 49y = 231 \quad \text{(iii)}$$
$$42x + 36y = 192 \quad \text{(iv)}$$
$$13y = 39$$
$$\mathbf{y = 3}$$

Substituting
$$6x + 21 = 33$$
$$6x = 12$$
$$\mathbf{x = 2}$$

(c)

$$3x - 9y = 0 \quad \text{(i)}$$
$$4x - 10y = 8 \quad \text{(ii)}$$

Multiply equation (i) by 4

Multiply equation (ii) by 3

$$12x - 36y = 0$$
$$12x - 30y = 24$$
$$\Rightarrow 6y = 24$$
$$\mathbf{y = 4}$$

Substituting
$$3x - 36 = 0$$
$$3x = 36$$
$$\mathbf{x = 12}$$

(d)

$$10x - 4y = 42 \quad \text{(i)}$$
$$6x + 2y = 34 \quad \text{(ii)}$$

Multiply equation (i) by 6

Multiply equation (ii) by 10

$$60x - 24y = 252 \quad \text{(iii)}$$
$$60x + 20y = 340 \quad \text{(iv)}$$
$$44y = 88$$
$$\mathbf{y = 2}$$

Substituting
$$10x - 8 = 42$$
$$10x = 50$$
$$\mathbf{x = 5}$$

(e)

$$x + 2y = 0 \quad \text{(i)}$$

$$4x - 2y = 50 \quad \text{(ii)}$$

Multiply equation (i) by 4

$$4x + 8y = 0 \quad \text{(iii)}$$

and

$$4x - 2y = 50 \quad \text{(ii)}$$

then

$$10y = -50$$

$$y = \mathbf{-5}$$

If

$$y = -5$$

$$x - 10 = 0$$

$$x = \mathbf{10}$$

SUMMARISING AND ANALYSING DATA

6 TYPES OF DATA

Tutorial note:

Without data, there would be no business statistics. This question is testing your knowledge on the various types of data.

(a) RAW DATA is the set of **observations** generated by a time series study, or by a cross-sectional study or by survey methods. The epithet *raw* is applied to the data in its state before it has been subjected to **any detailed statistical analysis**. Such data may merely be in the form of a list of cases which may have emerged in chronological order and in this form have no obvious meaning. The task of the statistician is to **arrange** the data in a more meaningful form by, for example, ordering it from highest value to lowest, by computing a measure of **central tendency** such as the arithmetic mean and by calculating a measure of dispersion such as the **standard deviation**. In this way, we may examine the distribution of values and perhaps be able to compare one distribution with another to see if they exhibit any statistically significant differences.

(b) SECONDARY DATA is data that has not been collected by the user specifically **for the purpose to which it is being put**. It should be contrasted with primary data. Primary data is data that has been collected by the user specifically for **its current purpose**. When using secondary data, the user must be aware of the method of collection and the use for which the data was originally collected. To ignore such things as the sampling method or, for example, the type of questionnaire used to collect the original data could result in the secondary user using data that is **inappropriate and biased** in some way.

(c) DISCRETE and CONTINUOUS DATA. There are two important types of variable quantity from the statistical viewpoint: those which vary discretely and those which vary continuously. A discrete variable is one which can take only a **finite** number of **distinct** values (eg examination marks ranging from 1 to 100). On the other hand, time is a continuous variable. Graphically, discrete variables are usually represented by a series of **distinct points**, whilst a continuous variable is represented by a **continuous line**. In practice, discrete variables are often treated as continuous. A variable which can theoretically assume any value between two given values is a **continuous** variable, otherwise it is a **discrete** variable. If a variable can assume only one value, it is called a **constant**.

7   PIGLET

Tutorial note:

Again this is a straightforward question but very time pressured. You only have 12 minutes to group the data together and then sketch the ogive. If you are running out of time in the exam, a tip is to find the highest values (in this case 112.6). This tells you what is the highest group you will require (£100 to £120k). You can then draw the axes on your graph paper (putting in titles, etc) and get the easy marks. You are told the groupings are at £20k intervals and so you should start by setting out a table for these groupings. Remember that cumulative percentages are asked for.

(a)

	1 Products	*2* Frequency	*3* Cumulative frequency	*4* Cumulative percentage
£0 to £19.9k	1, 12	2	2	10
£20.0k to £39.9k	4, 13, 15	3	5	25
£40.0k to £59.9k	3, 10, 16, 18	4	9	45
£60.0k to £79.9k	8, 9, 14, 17, 19	5	14	70
£80.0k to £99.9k	7, 11, 20	3	17	85
£100.0k to £119.9k	2, 5, 6	3	20	100
		20		

(b)

Cumulative percentage ogive for products sales

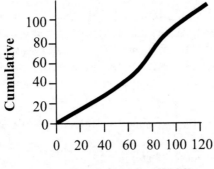

Product sales (£000)

(c)   An ogive represents a **cumulative frequency** distribution.

A decile represents **10%** of the population.

A percentile represents **1%** of the population.

8   DEPARTMENT STORES

Tutorial note:

Part (a) is a straightforward mean and median calculation which ought to generate full marks. It is in part (b) where marks are lost. Here you need to use your knowledge of statistics and the calculations you have made in part (a). To help you answer part (c) make full use of your mathematical table.

(a) (i) Mean value including all 67 cases

$$= \frac{\text{Total value of losses}}{\text{Total number of cases}}$$

$$= \frac{1,383,000}{67}$$

$$= \mathbf{£20,642}$$

Median value

$$= \frac{34 - 17}{18} \times 10,000$$

$$= \mathbf{£9,444}$$

(ii) Mean value excluding first class of 17 cases

$$= \frac{1,383,000}{50}$$

$$= \mathbf{£27,600}$$

Median value

$$= 10,000 + \frac{25.5 - 18}{11} \times 4,999$$

$$= \mathbf{£13,408}$$

(b) • Arithmetic mean is approximately **double** the median in both cases.

• This is because distribution leans to the **left** but has a longer tail to the **right** with higher values of the **variables**.

• A **quarter** of the frauds committed result in a zero loss.

• Under such situations arithmetic mean will always be **higher** than the median.

(c) The standard deviation is a measure of **dispersion** which indicates the **average** spread of all data items from the **mean**.

For ungrouped data the formula is:

$$SD = \sqrt{\frac{\Sigma(x - \bar{x})^2}{n}}$$

For grouped data the formula is:

$$SD = \sqrt{\frac{\Sigma fx^2}{\Sigma f} - \left(\frac{\Sigma fx}{\Sigma f}\right)^2}$$

A high value for the standard deviation indicates that the data is **widely** dispersed around the **mean**.

A low value indicates that the data is **clustered** quite closely around the **mean**.

9   SINBAD LTD

Tutorial note:

Question could not be more straightforward. Calculate Σfx and divide by Σf to get mean. Standard deviation formula from CIMA tables. Comments in part (c) based on findings in parts (a) and (b).

Lowest value £	Highest value £	Mid-point x	Frequency f	fx	fx²
0.00	0.99	0.495	274	135.63	67.14
1.00	1.99	1.495	518	774.41	1,157.74
2.00	2.99	2.495	594	1,482.03	3,697.66
3.00	3.99	3.495	756	2,642.22	9,234.56
4.00	4.99	4.495	386	1,735.07	7,799.14
5.00	5.99	5.495	168	923.16	5,072.76
6.00	6.99	6.495	104	675.48	4,387.24
			2,800	8,368.00	31,416.24
			$=\Sigma f$	$=\Sigma fx$	$=\Sigma fx^2$

(a)   Mean transaction value $= 8{,}368/2{,}800 = $ **£2.99**

(b)   Standard deviation

$$= \sqrt{\frac{31{,}416.24}{2{,}800} - (2.99)^2}$$

$$= \sqrt{11.22 - 8.94}$$

$$= \sqrt{2.28} = \textbf{£1.51}$$

(c)   The mean amount spent by customers has **risen** by **10** pence and the standard deviation by **12** pence.

The **increase** in the mean denotes that the **average spend** has risen over the period and the **increase** in standard deviation indicates that there is more **variability** in the level of purchaser.

10   MANAGER'S REPORT

(a)   A

$fx \quad = \quad f \times x$

$\qquad = \quad 40 \times 3$

$\therefore A \quad = \quad \textbf{120}$

B

$fx^2 \quad = \quad f \times x^2$

$\qquad = \quad 40 \times 9$

$\therefore B \quad = \quad \textbf{360}$

(b)   Mean $= \dfrac{\sum fx}{\sum f}$

$= \dfrac{420}{100}$

$= \mathbf{4.20}$

or mean $= 4.20 \times 1,000 = £4,200$

(c)   SD $= \sqrt{\dfrac{\sum fx^2}{\sum f} - \overline{x}^2}$

$= \sqrt{\dfrac{2,100}{100} - (4.2)^2}$

$= \sqrt{21 - 17.64}$

$= \sqrt{3.36}$

$\therefore$ SD $= 1.8330303$

or SD $= 1.8330303 \times 1,000 \approx £1,833$

(d)   (i)

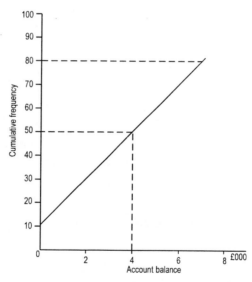

(ii)   Median, from the diagram, is where cumulative frequency $= 50, \approx £4,000$

(iii)   Semi-interquartile range $= \dfrac{Q_3 - Q_1}{2}$

From the ogive

$Q_1 = £2,900$ [25th percentile]

$Q_3 = £5,800$ [75th percentile]

$\therefore$ semi-interquartile range $= \dfrac{5,800 - 2,900}{2}$

$= £1,450$

(e)   As the data is skewed, both the standard deviation and the arithmetic mean will overestimate the average and spread of the balances. The median and the semi-interquartile range will therefore be the best summary measures.

PROBABILITY

11 PERISHABLE COMMODITIES

Tutorial note:

This is a straightforward probability and expected value question.

Step 1

Plot sales demand against quantity of stock bought and calculate the profit at each level.

(a)

Stock purchased	Sales demand			
	20 £	21 £	22 £	23 £
20	600	600	600	600
21	570	630	630	630
22	540	600	660	660
23	510	570	630	690

Sales demand	Probability	Stock purchased			
		20 EV	21 EV	22 EV	23 EV
20	0.2	120	114	108	102
21	0.4	240	252	240	228
22	0.3	180	189	198	189
23	0.1	60	63	66	69
		600	618	612	588

(b) Given that the wholesaler is seeking to **maximise** profits, he will order **21** cases per day which will yield an expected profit of **£618**, the highest of the available alternatives.

(c)

	Valid	Not valid

If there was no prior knowledge of the demand pattern, the wholesaler might make the following assumptions:

- If less cases are bought, they could be purchased at a lower price.

- Price could be held constant up to a certain time of day and then lowered to clear perishable stock.

- To operate a cautious purchasing policy until regular buying patterns were established, eg there may be daily or seasonal fluctuations.

12   PORCELAIN MANUFACTURER

Tutorial note:

Questions on probability theory should be attempted wherever possible since they are quick to calculate if you know how to do it and you will always be up against the clock in this paper.

(a)   **Step 1**

Apply ratios:

1X:2Y:3Z   =   6

therefore   X   = $\dfrac{240 \times 1}{6}$ =   **40**

Y   = $\dfrac{240 \times 2}{6}$ =   **80**

Z   = $\dfrac{240 \times 3}{6}$ =   **120**

(b)

X	Sample	40	Good	38	Bad	2
Y	Sample	80	Good	72	Bad	8
Z	Sample	120	Good	84	Bad	36
		240		194		46

Probability of plate being defective   = $\dfrac{46}{240}$ = **0.192**

(c)   There are 46 defective plates.

36 come from Z so probability that it comes from Z   = $\dfrac{36}{46}$ = **0.783**

(d)   Mutually exclusive events cannot happen **simultaneously**, eg if you toss a coin once getting a head or a tail is **mutually exclusive**. It is either one or the other.

An independent event is one that, if it happens it has **no effect** on another event occurring, eg **rolling a dice** and **drawing from a pack of cards**.

13   TRAVEL AGENCY I

Tutorial note:

The first 12 marks of this question should be within most students' grasp. However, please show all workings and where figures came from. You might make a numerical error but can still get marks for technique.

(a)   Probability that a European brochure is selected.

Number of European brochures   =   285

Number of brochures in stock   =   500

Thus 285 chance in 500   = $\dfrac{285}{500}$ = **0.57**

(b)   Probability that an African brochure is not selected.

There are two ways of attempting this question:

Turn the question on its head and ask: what is the probability of an African brochure being selected.

Number of African brochures	=	15
Number of brochures in stock	=	500
Thus 15 chance in 500	=	0.03
Therefore chance of not being selected	=	1 – 0.03 = **0.97**

Proof

If African brochure is not selected then brochure could be:

European	=	285
American	=	90
or Asian	=	110

Therefore probability of selecting one of these is:

$$\frac{285+90+110}{500} = \frac{485}{500} \qquad = \qquad 0.97$$

(c)   If neither an American, nor an Asian brochure is selected then it will have to be either:

European	=	285
or African	=	15

Therefore probability of selecting one of these is:

$$\frac{285+15}{500} = \frac{300}{500} \qquad = \qquad \textbf{0.6}$$

(d)   Probability that either a European or an Asian brochure is selected:

Number of European brochures	=	285
Number of Asian brochures	=	110
	=	$\frac{395}{500} = \textbf{0.79}$

(e)   The expected value EV is a probability weighted average of the value of each outcome where:

EV = Σpx where x = **value of an outcome** p = **probability of outcome**

(f)   *Advantages of using expected values in decision making*

   (i)   Using expected values is an objective way of reaching a decision.

   (ii)   Where decisions are made on a regular basis, it is as good as any method.

   (iii)   Over a period of time, the outcomes will average out in accordance with the probabilities set.

(g)   *Disadvantages of using expected values in decision making*

   (i)   If events only happen once or twice there can be no long-term average.

   (ii)   Expected values are dependent on probability and cash flow estimates.

   (iii)   Based solely on quantitative information. Ignores social, environmental and other issues.

14   SAMPLING THEORY

(a)   SIMPLE RANDOM SAMPLING

This is a method in which **every** member of a population has an **equal** chance of being chosen in the sample.   One way this can be achieved is by numbering every member of a population, putting their numbers into a hat; in practice this would be carried out by computer. If a sample is to be fair, it is necessary for some sort of **random** sampling to be used.

STRATIFIED SAMPLING

If our population consists of a collection of different **groups**, then we can extend the idea of random sampling so that our population is split into these sub-**groups** and a random sample taken from the different sub-**groups**. If a population has sub-**groups** within it, then this is the most reliable method of sampling.

QUOTA SAMPLING

In this method you specify how many **people or items within a certain group** you want to sample, ie set a quota, then collect data from anyone or anything that **fits the required category** until the quota is filled. This method is widely used by interviewers **but** is the **least** accurate of sampling methods.

(b)   The proportion of 0.475 equates to a Z value of 1.960.

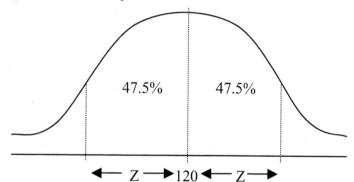

Required range   = $\bar{x} \pm 1.96 \sqrt{\dfrac{400}{100}}$

                  = 120 ± 3.92

or   =   **116.08 to 123.92 minutes**

15   TELEPHONE SALES STAFF

Tutorial note:

Initially, candidates may have been thrown by this question because the figures given in the question are usually figures you are asked to work out. However, with CIMA mathematical tables at your disposal, this is a very easy question, especially since it is broken into five short questions.

(a) Mean $= \dfrac{\sum fx}{\sum f} = \dfrac{30,000}{1,000} = \mathbf{30}$

(b) Standard deviation $= \sqrt{\dfrac{\sum fx^2}{\sum f} - \left(\dfrac{\sum fx}{\sum f}\right)^2}$

$$= \sqrt{\dfrac{994,400}{1,000} - \left(\dfrac{30,000}{1,000}\right)^2}$$

$$= \sqrt{994.4 - 900}$$

$$= \mathbf{9.72}$$

(c) Draw normal distribution

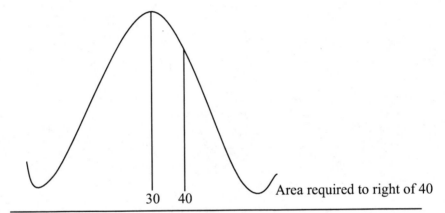

30   40

Area required to right of 40

Probability of more than 40

$\dfrac{40 - 30}{9.72}$ $\quad = \quad$ 1.03

See normal distribution tables $\quad = \quad$ 0.3485

Therefore, probability of more than 40 $\quad = \quad$ 0.5 – 0.3485 = **15.15%**

(d) Probability of between 15 and 25

Step 1

Probability of less than 15 $\quad \dfrac{15 - 30}{9.72} \quad = \quad$ 1.54

From normal distribution tables $\quad = \quad$ 0.50 – 0.4382 = 0.0618

Step 2

Probability of more than 25 $\quad \dfrac{25 - 30}{9.72} \quad = \quad$ 0.51

$\quad = \quad$ 0.1950 *(normal tables)*

Therefore, probability of being between 15 and 25

$$= \quad 0.5 - (0.1950 + 0.0618)$$

$$= \quad 0.2432$$

$$= \quad \mathbf{24\%}$$

(e)   •   The average number of calls made over a period.

•   By how much this average can fluctuate.

FINANCIAL MATHEMATICS

16   RESERVE FUNDS AND MORTGAGES

Tutorial note:

On the surface this appears to be a difficult question. Although parts (a) and (b) are independent, they can both be answered by applying the formula you are given. Reserve funds and mortgages are similar in that they follow a geometric series. By applying the correct numbers to the formulae, the calculations are actually quite simple.

(a)   Let x be the sum put away at equal intervals.

The first sum will be invested for 12 quarters.

The rate is 2% per quarter so investment will be $x(1.02)^{12}$

The second sum will be invested for 11 quarters.

The rate is 2% per quarter so investment will be $x(1.02)^{11}$

The final sum will be invested for 1 quarter.

The rate is 2% per quarter so investment will be $x(1.02)^{1}$

Reserve fund total $= x(1.02)^{12} + x(1.02)^{11} + \ldots + x(1.02)^{1} = 500,000$

This is a geometric series where:

N   =   12 (number of terms)

A   =   x(1.02) where A is first term

R   =   1.02 (common ratio)

so using formula $S = \dfrac{A(R^{N} - 1)}{(R - 1)}$

$$500,000 \quad = \quad \frac{x(1.02)(1.02^{12} - 1)}{(1.02 - 1)}$$

$$= \quad \frac{0.2736x}{0.02}$$

$$= \quad 13.68x$$

then x   =   £36,550

so the sum of **£36,550** will need to be put away.

(b)   10 years is 40 quarters.

 (i)   Using compound interest $£100,000 \times (1.03)^{40}$ =   **£326,204**

 (ii)   Using geometric progression   £326,204   = $\dfrac{A(1.03^{40}-1)}{(1.03-1)}$

     =   75.4013A

     $\therefore$ A   =   £4,326

     ie Quarterly mortgage payment   =   **£4,326**

(iii)   Quarterly rate 3%

 Annual rate   = $(1.03)^4 - 1$

     =   0.12551

     =   **12.551%**

17   INTEREST AND COMPOUND INTEREST

Tutorial note:

This question is an attempt to introduce you gradually to simple and compound interest. Parts (b) to (e) are more likely to appear in the multiple choice questions of the paper but it is vital that you understand the workings of interest rates before you are able to attempt questions on discounted cash flows.

(a)   **Simple interest: £100 invested at a rate of interest of 6% for a year would yield £106: our original investment of £100 plus £6 interest.**

 With compound interest, the interest is added each year to the principal so, after 3 years, a £100 investment at 10% would become:

After year 1	**£100 + £10**	**=**	**£110**
After year 2	**£110 + £11**	**=**	**£121**
After year 3	**£121 + £12.10**	**=**	**£133.10**

(b) i =   xrn

 where   r   =   rate of interest

     i   =   interest

     x   =   initial sum invested

     n   =   time in years

 then   i   =   xrn $= 5,000 \times 0.12 \times 5 = $ **£3,000**

(c)   r   = $\dfrac{i}{xn}$

 then   r   = $\dfrac{400}{800 \times 10} = 0.05 = $ **5%**

(d)   We need to use the formula:

$x(1 + r)^n$

The value of £625 invested at 4% per annum over 10 years

$$= £625 (1 + 0.04)^{10}$$

$$= £625 (1.04)^{10}$$

$$= £925$$

So compound interest element

$$= £925 - 625 = \textbf{£300}$$

(e)   Using the same formula:

$$v = x(1 + r)^n$$

$$\text{then } £10,000 = x (1 + 0.05)^{10}$$

$$\text{ie } x = \frac{£10,000}{(1.05)^{10}}$$

$$x = £6,139$$

so **£6,139** will need to be invested today.

18   HOSPITAL MAINTENANCE COSTS

Tutorial note:

This is a question on discounted cash flows where there are a lot of marks to be picked up in a short period of time.

Marks are very generous for part (b), assuming part (a) is answered correctly.

(a)

Time period	Cost £	6% discount factor	Discounted cash flow £
0	3,000	1	3,000
1	3,500	0.943	3,300.50
2	4,000	0.890	3,560
3	12,000	0.840	10,080
4	4,000	0.792	3,168
5	4,500	0.747	3,361.50
6	5,000	0.705	3,525
7	13,000	0.665	8,645
			38,640

(b)   The maximum fixed annual charge that could be made is that which has the same present value over the period.

The cumulative DCF figure is £38,640. The cumulative 6% discount factor is 6.582.

$$\text{So } \frac{£38,640}{6,582} = £5,870.56$$

Therefore **£5,870.56** is maximum annual charge.

(c)

Tutorial note:

There will be more than 5 scoring points on a question like this but there are only 5 marks on offer so one mark for each relevant point.

Factors which need to be considered:

- **Redundancy costs might outweigh any potential savings.**
- **A hospital is a public service, maximum profits may not be the key issue here.**
- **Would private contractors be able to do a proper job?**
- **What effect would contracting out have on the rest of the hospital staff?**
- **If it goes to competitive tender, management time and expense may be involved.**
- **How can an independent contract company guarantee costs?**

Examiner's note:

There are arguments both for and against contracting out but the wording of this question was loaded against.

19 PRODUCT LIFE CYCLE

Tutorial note:

Part (a) is a straightforward cash flow question which does not even take into account the discount factor.

Part (b) carries on from part (a) when a discount factor of 8% is applied.

Part (c) is a definition question which asks why DCF techniques are used in appraising investment decisions.

(a)

Year	Cash flow (£)
1	56,000
2	57,120
3	59,976
4	65,794
5	72,571
6	79,828
7	83,819
8	82,981
9	80,492
10	76,467

(b)   **Net present value of cash flows at 8%**

Year	Cash flow (from part (a)) £	Discount factor	DCF
1	56,000	0.926	51,856
2	57,120	0.857	48,952
3	59,976	0.794	47,621
4	65,974	0.735	48,491
5	72,571	0.681	49,421
6	79,828	0.630	50,292
7	83,819	0.583	48,866
8	82,981	0.540	44,810
9	80,492	0.500	40,246
10	76,467	0.463	35,404
			465,959

Maximum amount company could invest to meet 8% is **£465,959**.

(c)   Discounting is carried out in investment appraisal decisions because cash today has a greater value today than at some period in the future.

This is because:

1   **Money has an opportunity cost. £1,000 invested today would receive a rate of interest.**

2   **Uncertainty – there is no guarantee that money invested in a project today will generate the amount of income expected.**

3   **Time preference. To quote the great 20th century economist, John Maynard Keynes, 'In the long-run, we are all dead'.**

20   LOAN

(a)   **A**

Interest charged in year 2

In year 1, interest charged   =   £50,000 × 0.09

                                  =   £4,500

So at the start of year 2, the loan outstanding is

£50,000 + £4,500   =   £54,500

Interest charged in year 2   =   £54,500 × 0.09

                                 =   **£4,905**

B

Outstanding debt in year 5

Using S   = $x(1 + r)^n$, we have

        S   = $50,000 (1 + 0.09)^5$

              =   **£76,931.20**

C

Interest earned in year 4

Using $\dfrac{A(R^n - 1)}{R - 1}$ to find the amount in the fund at the end of year 3, we have

$$\dfrac{13{,}922.61\left((1.05)^3 - 1\right)}{1.05 - 1} \qquad = \qquad £43{,}89103$$

$\therefore$ Interest gained in year 4 $\qquad = \qquad 43{,}891.03 \times 0.05$

$\qquad\qquad\qquad\qquad\qquad\qquad = \qquad$ **£2,914.55**

D

Amount in fund in year 2

$$= \qquad 13{,}922.61$$
$$+ \ 13{,}922.61$$
$$+ \ 13{,}922.61 \times 0.05$$
$$= \qquad \textbf{£28,541.35}$$

(b)   (i)   Using a geometric progression

$$S_n \qquad\qquad = \qquad \dfrac{A(R^n - 1)}{R - 1}$$

When $A = 1$, $R = 1.035$, $n = 17$

$$S_n \qquad\qquad = \qquad X\left(\dfrac{(1.035)^{17} - 1}{1.035 - 1}\right)$$

$$80{,}000 \qquad = \qquad X\left(\dfrac{0.794676}{0.035}\right)$$

$$= \qquad 22.70502 X xxxxxxxxxxxxx$$

$$X \qquad\qquad = \qquad \dfrac{80{,}000}{22.70502}$$

$$= \qquad 3{,}523.451$$

$$\approx \qquad \textbf{£3,523.45}$$

(ii)   Using the formula

$$S \qquad\qquad = \qquad X[1 + r]^n, \text{ where X is the present value}$$

and rearranging for X gives

$$X \qquad\qquad = \qquad S[1 + r]^{-n}$$

$$= \qquad 80{,}000 \,[1 + 0.035]^{-16}$$

$$= \qquad 46{,}136.47$$

$$\therefore \text{ PV} \qquad = \qquad \textbf{£46,136.47}$$

FORECASTING

21 TRAVEL AGENCY II

Tutorial note:

The key to answering a question of this nature is selecting the appropriate formula from the CIMA formulae sheet.

(a) If x = the number of bookings

y = the number of complaints

$$b = \frac{n \Sigma xy - (\Sigma x)(\Sigma y)}{n \Sigma x^2 - (\Sigma x)^2}$$

$$a = \bar{y} - b\bar{x}$$

where $\bar{y}$ = the mean y value

and $\bar{x}$ = the mean x value

x	y	x^2	xy
246	94	60,516	23,124
192	80	36,864	15,360
221	106	48,841	23,426
385	183	148,225	70,455
416	225	173,056	93,600
279	162	77,841	45,198
343	191	117,649	65,513
582	252	338,724	146,664
610	291	372,100	177,510
674	310	424,276	208,940
3,948	1,894	1,828,092	869,790

$\bar{x}$ = 394.8 $\bar{y}$ = 189.4

$$b = \frac{(10 \times 869{,}790) - (3{,}948 \times 1{,}894)}{(10 \times 1{,}828{,}092) - (3{,}948 \times 3{,}948)}$$

$$= \frac{1{,}220{,}388}{2{,}694{,}216}$$

$$= \mathbf{0.453}$$

a = $189.4 - (0.453 \times 394.8)$ = **10.56**

therefore y = $10.56 + 0.453x$

(b) y = $10.56 + (0.453 \times 750)$ = **350**

Examiner's tip:

It would be impossible to get full marks in part (b) unless the whole of part (a) was correct. However, you would be given marks for correct technique.

(c)   Linear regression could be used to give a reliable forecast on the number of complaints but there are a number of factors to consider.

- **A sample of 10 is too small on which to base this analysis.**

- **The number of 750 bookings is outside the range of data at our disposal.**

- **There is no reason to suggest that this linear relationship will remain constant.**

22   SALE OF PRODUCT X

Tutorial note:

To complete the analysis in part (a), we require an eight quarter total in column 5 and a moving average.

The first figure 185 in column 4 comes from the first four quarter sales units in column 3, ie 40 + 53 + 74 + 18.

The figures in column 5 come from pairs of figures in column 4.

The moving averages are calculated by dividing the figures in column 5 by 8.

In part (b), where you have to make seasonal adjustments, you need to subtract the seasonal factors. Remember that subtracting a negative figure is equivalent to adding a positive figure (eg a seasonal adjustment of –4.1 in quarter 2 of 20X6 is below yearly average so value needs adjusting upwards).

(a)

Year	Quarter	Sales (units)	Sum of fours	Centred 8 quarterly total	Moving average
20X6	2	40			
	3	53			
			185		
	4	74		372	46.50
			187		
20X7	1	18		372	46.50
			185		
	2	42		373	46.62
			188		
	3	51		378	47.25
			190		
	4	77		383	47.87
			193		
20X8	1	20		388	48.50
			195		
	2	45		388	48.50
			193		
	3	53		384	48.50
			191		
	4	75			
20X9	1	18			

(b) Seasonally-adjusted demand

Year	Quarter	Sales units	Seasonal adjustment	Seasonally-adjusted demand
20X6	2	40	−4.1	44.1
	3	53	+4.3	48.7
	4	74	+28.3	45.7
20X7	1	18	−28.5	46.5
	2	42	−4.1	46.1
	3	51	+4.3	46.7
	4	77	+28.3	48.7
20X8	1	20	−28.5	48.5
	2	45	−4.1	49.1
	3	53	+4.3	48.7
	4	75	+23.8	46.7
20X9	1	18	−28.5	46.5

(c) **Additive model assumes the seasonal factor for any quarter is always the same. Multiplicative model is better where trend is increasing or decreasing over time, because seasonal variations alter similarly.**

23   SALES FORECAST

(a)

Week	Day	Receipts	Five day moving total	Trend
1	1	8		
	2	12		
	3	15	54	10.8
	4	10	56	11.2
	5	9	57	11.4
2	1	10	59	11.8
	2	13	64	12.8
	3	17	71	14.2
	4	15	78	15.6
	5	16	88	17.6
3	1	17	96	19.2
	2	23	102	20.4
	3	25	107	21.4
	4	21	116	23.2
	5	21	123	24.6
4	1	26	130	26.0
	2	30	143	28.6
	3	32	157	31.4
	4	34		
	5	35		

PAPER C3 : BUSINESS MATHEMATICS

(b)   Within a four week period the trend has risen from 10.8 to 31.4.

Implications for management:

- **may require more stock.**

- **may require more staff.**

- **may require other resources.**

(c)   Seasonally-adjusted data shows the effect of non-seasonal influences by removing seasonal variations.

Example 1

Unemployment tends to rise in the summer as a new round of school and university leavers join the labour market. Since most elections are held in the summer, governments want to adjust these figures downwards.

Example 2

Some goods and services are faced with variations in seasonal demand, eg department stores sell more of their products in the run up to Christmas so sales will be adjusted downwards during this period and upwards when business is more slack.

184   FTC FOULKS LYNCH

Section 5

MOCK ASSESSMENT QUESTIONS

TIME ALLOWED 90 MINUTES

TOTAL MARKS 100

Question 1 is based on the following information.

The marketing department estimates that if the selling price of a new product is set at £40 per unit, sales will be 400 units per week. If the selling price is £20 per unit, sales will be 800 units per week.

The production department estimate that variable costs will be £7.50 per unit and fixed costs £10,000 per week.

---

1   (i)   The cost equation is [   ] .

      (ii)   The sales revenue equation is [   ] .

2   (i)   If $3x + 4y = 25$ and $10x + 2y = 38$, what are the values of x and y?

         $x =$ [   ]

         $y =$ [   ]

      (ii)   The shape of a graph of linear equation will be:

         A   U shaped

         B   Straight line

         C   L shaped

         D   Depends on linear equation

3   Equipment is sold for £240 and makes a profit of 20% on cost.

     What is the cost price?   [£   ]

4   If sales are £500 per week and cost of sales are £300 per week, gross profit expressed as a percentage is [%] .

5   Alex, Dave and John are in partnership and profits are split in the ratio 7:6:5. If profit for the year is £36,000, how much does Alex receive? [   ]

---

6   Three years ago Smith Bros purchased a van for £12,000. If they depreciate the vehicle by 25% on a reducing balance basis, the value of the vehicle at the end of year 3 is £ ☐ to the nearest pound.

7   (i)   A biased error arises when:

       ☐   individual items are rounded in the same direction.

       ☐   individual items are rounded in either direction.

       ☐   individual items are rounded in the opposite direction.

       ☐   individual items are not rounded.

    (ii)   An unbiased error arises when:

       ☐   individual items are rounded in the same direction.

       ☐   individual items are rounded in either direction.

       ☐   individual items are rounded in the opposite direction.

       ☐   individual items are not rounded.

8   The main advantage of using a discounted cash flow approach to investment appraisal over more traditional methods is:

       ☐   it is easier to calculate.

       ☐   it is easier to understand.

       ☐   it will show a higher profit figure.

       ☐   it is a technique which recognises the time value of money.

9   If a statistician selects two of their ten sales regions and then one in five customers from each of these two regions, this is an example of what type of sampling? ☐

10   An ogive represents a cumulative frequency distribution on which can be shown ranges of values containing given proportions of the total population.

    (i)   The upper quartile represents:

       ☐   25% through the cumulative frequencies.

       ☐   75% through the cumulative frequencies.

       ☐   1% of the population.

       ☐   10% of the population.

(ii)   The decile represents:

| | 1% of the population. |

| | 10% of the population. |

| | the majority of the population. |

| | 90% of the population. |

(iii)   Cumulative frequencies are plotted against:

| | the mid-point. |

| | the lower class boundaries. |

| | the upper class boundaries. |

| | any of the above. |

11   A frequency distribution of a sample of monthly incomes is as follows:

£	Frequency
400 and less than 800	7
800 and less than 1,000	16
1,000 and less than 1,200	28
1,200 and less than 1,300	21
1,300 and less than 1,400	8
	80

If the area between £800 and £1,000 has a height of 8 cm, what is the height of the rectangle representing 1,000 – 1,200?

12   (i)   The arithmetic mean of 3, 6, 10, 14, 17, 19 and 22 is

        (ii)   The median of 3, 6, 10, 14, 17, 19 and 22 is

        (iii)   The mode is the value:

| | which appears most frequently. |

| | which is the same as the arithmetic mean. |

| | which is the mid-point value. |

| | none of the above. |

13 If there are n items in the distribution, the median is the:

☐ $\dfrac{n+1}{2}$ term

☐ $\dfrac{n-1}{2}$ term

☐   n + 1 term

☐   n – 1 term

14 A sample of 12 packets of crisps taken from a box had the following weights in grammes:

504, 506, 501, 505, 507, 506, 504, 508, 503, 505, 502, 504

(i)   Calculate the mean weight ☐

(ii)   Calculate the median weight ☐

(iii)   Calculate the modal weight ☐

15 The standard deviation of 3, 5, 8, 11 and 13 is ☐ to two decimal places.

16 If the standard deviation is 1.1 and the arithmetic mean is 3.5 then the coefficient of variation is equal to ☐ to two decimal places.

17 If a commodity costs £2.60 today and £3.68 in one year's time, by what percentage has the price risen in the intervening period? ☐ %

18 A pack of cards consists of 52 playing cards.

(i)   What is the probability that a card selected at random is the ace of hearts? ☐

(ii)   What is the probability that a card selected at random is an ace? ☐

(iii)   What is the probability that a card selected at random is a heart? ☐

19 The following data relates to a number of CIMA students who recently sat Paper C3.

Type of student	Total number of scripts	Total number of passes
Male	1,000	500
Female	500	300

(i)   If a student is selected at random what is the probability that they failed?

☐   1 in 2

☐   1 in 3

☐   7 in 15

☐   8 in 15

(ii)   If a student is selected at random what is the probability that the student is male or someone who failed?

20   If the three possible outcomes of a decision are profits of £10, £50 and £80 with probabilities of 0.3, 0.3 and 0.4, what is the expected profit?   £

21   A box contains three colours of ball: 4 red, 3 yellow and 5 blue. Three balls are selected at random and there is no replacement between each selection. What is the probability of selecting one of each colour?

   (to two decimal places)

22   10% of golf balls have a minor defect. They are packaged in boxes of six. What is the probability that a box selected at random has no defects?

   (to two decimal places)

23   A group of workers have a weekly wage which is normally distributed with a mean of £360 per week and a standard deviation of £15.

(i)   What is the probability a worker earns more than £380?   %

(ii)   What is the probability a worker earns less than £330?   %

24   Electricity costs based on production levels would tend to be:

   Perfect positive linear

   Perfect negative linear

   High positive

   Low negative

25   The figures below relate to the number of daily visitors to a hotel aggregated by quarter.

	Quarter 1	Quarter 2	Quarter 3	Quarter 4
20X0	-	-	-	88
20X1	90	120	200	28
20X2	22	60	164	16
20X3	10	80	192	-

(i)   The first figure to appear in the 4 quarter total is   .

(ii)   The first figure to appear in the 8 quarter total is   .

(iii)   The average seasonal variation for the second quarter in 20X1 was   .

26   An item costs £59.99 inclusive of VAT at 17.5%. What is the price exclusive of VAT to the nearest penny?

27 The sum of money which, if invested now at 6% per annum compound interest, will be worth £20,000 in 10 years' time is: £ [   ]

28 The solution to the simultaneous equations:

$2y = 4x + 13$

$y = 5x - 4$

is: x = [   ]

y = [   ]

29 A leisure centre wants to improve the services it provides to the community at certain times of the day. A sample of users was taken and the age of users recorded as follows:

Age	Frequency
0 and less than 20	20
20 and less than 30	48
30 and less than 40	104
40 and less than 50	68
50 and less than 80	36

(i) In a histogram for this data, the height of the 20 – 30 class is 12 cm. The height of the 0 – 20 class is [   ] to two decimal places.

(ii) The mean of the data is [   ] to one decimal place.

(iii) The standard deviation of the data is [   ] to one decimal place.

30 In a positively skewed distribution the:

[   ] mean is less than the median.

[   ] mode is greater than the median.

[   ] median is less than the mode.

[   ] mean is greater than the mode.

31 The underlying trend of sales is $y = 550 + 2.67x$, where y = number of units sold and x represents the time period.

(i) If period 12 has a seasonal variation of +52.8 then the sales forecast of that period, assuming an additive forecasting model, is [   ] .

(ii) If period 14 has a seasonal variation of −24% then the sales forecast for that period, assuming a multiplicative model, is [   ] .

32 If $\Sigma x = 86$, $\Sigma y = 48$, $\Sigma x^2 = 3,364$, $\Sigma xy = 4,860$ and n = 12, what is the value of b in the regression line of y on x where the line is in the form $y = a + bx$?

b = [   ] to three decimal places.

33   The correlation coefficient between sales and profit is found to be 0.78. How much of the variation in profit is explained by the variation in sales?

⬚   to one decimal place.

34   Products passing through a process are known to contain faults. 1% contain serious faults and are scrapped, 2% can be reworked and 5% require minor adjustments. What is the probability that a randomly chosen item will be fault free?

⬚   to two decimal places.

35   A train company is allowed to raise fare prices by 4% per annum. If a current ticket price is £15.60, what will be the price in 5 years, to the nearest penny?   ⬚

Section 6

ANSWERS TO MOCK ASSESSMENT QUESTIONS

1 (i) Total cost   =   Fixed cost + Variable cost

   =   **£10,000 + 7.5x** where x is number of units

(ii) Let price per unit =   £p/unit

Sales Q   =   a + bp

From the information given:

400   =   a + 40b   (i)

800   =   a + 20b   (ii)

Then (ii) − (i) gives:

400   =   −20b

ie b   =   −20

Substituting in (i)

400   =   a + 40 × (−20)

So a   =   1,200

Then Q   =   1,200 − 20p

ie 20p   =   1,200 − Q

$$p \quad = \quad \frac{1,200 - Q}{20}$$

$$p \quad = \quad 60 - \frac{Q}{20}$$

Then sales revenue =   Q × p

$$= \quad Q \times \left(60 - \frac{Q}{20}\right)$$

$$= \quad \mathbf{60Q - \frac{Q^2}{20}}$$

2 (i)

$$3x + 4y = 25 \quad \text{(i)}$$
$$10x + 2y = 38 \quad \text{(ii)}$$

Multiply equation (ii) by 2

$$20x + 4y = 76 \quad \text{(iii)}$$

(iii) − (i) gives:

$$17x = 51$$
$$\text{ie } x = 3$$

Substituting in (i)

$$9 + 4y = 25$$
$$4y = 16$$
$$y = 4$$

So **x = 3 y = 4**

(ii) **B**

3 If cost price = 100%

then selling price is 120% of cost (since profit is 20% on cost)

120% of cost	=	£240
100% of cost	=	$240 \times \dfrac{100}{120}$
ie cost price	≈	**£200**

4

Profit = £500 − £300	=	£200
Gross profit	=	$\dfrac{200}{500}$
	=	**40%**

5

Total profit to be distributed	=	£36,000
Alex's share	=	$\dfrac{7}{18} \times £36,000$
	=	**£14,000**

6

	Depreciation	Value
Year 1	3,000	9,000
Year 2	2,250	6,750
Year 3	1,687.50	5,062.50

ie value at end of Year 3 ≈ **£5,063**

7 (i) A biased error arises when individual items are rounded in the same direction.

(ii) An unbiased error arises when individual items are rounded in either direction.

8 It is a technique which recognises the time value of money.

9 Cluster sampling.

10   (i)   75% through the cumulative frequencies.

       (ii)   10% of the population.

       (iii)   The upper class boundaries.

11   Since frequency of 16 has height of 8 cm, scale is 1 cm for 2 frequencies.

       Then frequency of 28 should have a height of **14 cms**.

12   (i) $\dfrac{3+6+10+14+17+19+22}{7} = \dfrac{91}{7}$

       ∴ Mean = **13**

       (ii)   Median is the value of the middle item.

       Hence Median = **14**

       (iii)   The mode is the value which appears most frequently.

13   The median is the $\dfrac{n+1}{2}$ **term**

14   (i)   To make calculation easier subtract 500 from each of the weights as follows:

       Mean $= \dfrac{(500 \times 12) + 4 + 6 + 1 + 5 + 7 + 6 + 4 + 8 + 3 + 5 + 2 + 4}{12}$

       $= 500 + \dfrac{55}{12} = \mathbf{504.6}$

       (ii)   Arranging in numerical order we have:

       501, 502, 503, 504, 504, 504, 505, 505, 506, 506, 507, 508

       Median $= \dfrac{504 + 505}{2} = \mathbf{504.5}$

       (iii)   Mode   =   **504** since it appears 3 times

15

x	x^2
3	9
5	25
8	64
11	121
13	169
$\Sigma x = 40$	$\Sigma x^2 = 388$

Standard deviation $= \sqrt{\dfrac{388}{5} - \left(\dfrac{40}{5}\right)^2}$

$= \sqrt{77.6 - 64}$

$= \sqrt{13.6} = \mathbf{3.69}$

16   Coefficient of variation $= \dfrac{\text{Standard deviation} \times 100}{\text{Arithmetic mean}}$

$= \dfrac{110}{3.5} = \mathbf{31.43}$

17   Price rise = £3.68 − £2.60   =   £1.08

Percentage rise $= \dfrac{1.08}{2.60} \times 100$

$= \mathbf{41.5\%}$

18   (i)   Only one ace of hearts in pack of 53, so probability is $\dfrac{\mathbf{1}}{\mathbf{52}}$

(ii)   There are 4 aces in pack of 52 so probability is $\dfrac{4}{52}$ or $\dfrac{\mathbf{1}}{\mathbf{13}}$

(iii)   There are 13 hearts in pack of 52 so probability is $\dfrac{13}{52}$ or $\dfrac{\mathbf{1}}{\mathbf{4}}$

19   (i) $\dfrac{\text{Total failures}}{\text{Total students}} = \dfrac{700}{1,500} = \dfrac{\mathbf{7}}{\mathbf{15}}$

(ii)   Turn question round. Someone who is not male and passed is a female who passed.

Probability $= \dfrac{300}{1,500} = \dfrac{1}{5}$

Therefore the opposite is $1 - \dfrac{1}{5} = \dfrac{\mathbf{4}}{\mathbf{5}}$

20   Expected profit = 0.3 × £10 + 0.3 × £50 + 0.4 × £80   =   £3 + £15 + £32

=   **£50**

21   There are 6 possible ways that give one of each colour.

Possibility	Ball 1	Ball 2	Ball 3
1	red	yellow	blue
2	red	blue	yellow
3	yellow	red	blue
4	yellow	blue	red
5	blue	red	yellow
6	blue	yellow	red

$P(1) = \dfrac{4}{12} \times \dfrac{3}{11} \times \dfrac{5}{10} = \dfrac{60}{1,320}$

$P(2) = \dfrac{4}{12} \times \dfrac{5}{11} \times \dfrac{3}{10} = \dfrac{60}{1,320}$

Similarly:

$P(3) = \dfrac{60}{1,320}$

$P(4) = \dfrac{60}{1,320}$

$$P(5) = \frac{60}{1,320}$$

$$P(6) = \frac{60}{1,320}$$

P (one of each colour)

$$= \left(\frac{60}{1,320}\right) \times 6$$

$$= \frac{360}{1,320}$$

$$= \frac{3}{11} \text{ or } \mathbf{0.27}$$

22 $\left(\dfrac{9}{10}\right)^6 = \mathbf{0.53}$

23 (i) $Z = \dfrac{380 - 360}{15}$ $= 1.33$

From table Z $= .4082$

So probability > £380 $= 0.5 - 0.4082$

$= 0.0918$ or approx **9%**

(ii) $Z = \dfrac{330 - 360}{15}$ $= -2$

From table Z $= .4772$

So probability < £330 $= 0.5 - 0.4772$

$= 0.0228$ or approx **2%**

24 Perfect positive linear, ie rise by a constant amount.

25 (i) $88 + 90 + 120 + 200 = 498$

∴ First 4 quarter total is **498**.

(ii) $498 + 90 + 120 + 200 + 28 = 498 + 438 = 936$

∴ First 8 quarter total is **936**.

(iii) 8 quarter average = $936 \div 8 =$ 117

Actual 2nd quarter 120

Variation **3**

26 $£59.99 \times \dfrac{100}{117.5}$

$= £51.055 = \mathbf{£51.06}$ to the nearest penny.

27 V = $x(1 + r)^n$ where V = £20,000

r = 0.06

n = 10

$\therefore x$ = $\dfrac{£20,000}{(1 + .06)^{10}}$

=   **£11,168**

28 $2y$ = $4x + 13$ (i)

y = $5x - 4$ (ii)

Multiply (ii) by 2

$2y$ = $10x - 8$ (iii)

Then (iii) – (i) gives:

0 = $6x - 21$

$6x$ = 21

x = 3.5

Substituting in (ii)

y = $(5 \times 3.5) - 4 = 13.5$

so **x = 3.5 and y = 13.5**

29   (i)   The 20 – 30 class is 12 cm high with a frequency of 48, therefore each cm represents a frequency of 4.

In a histogram you are comparing the area of the bar not the height. The 0 – 20 class is twice as wide as the 20 – 30 class therefore the height needs to be multiplied by ½.

Frequency for 0 – 20 class is 20. Therefore required height = $\dfrac{20}{4} \times \dfrac{1}{2}$

= **2.50** to two decimal places.

(ii)

Mid-point x	f	fx
10	20	200
25	48	1,200
35	104	3,640
45	68	3,060
65	36	2,340
	276	10,440

Mean = $\dfrac{\sum fx}{\sum f} = \dfrac{10,440}{276} =$ **37.8** to one decimal place

(iii)

Mid-point x	x^2	fx^2
10	100	2,000
25	625	30,000
35	1,225	127,400
45	2,025	137,700
65	4,225	152,100
	8,200	449,200

Standard deviation, σ $\quad = \quad \sqrt{\dfrac{\sum fx^2}{\sum f} - \left(\dfrac{\sum fx}{\sum f}\right)^2}$

$$= \quad \sqrt{\dfrac{449,200}{276} - \left(\dfrac{10,440}{276}\right)^2}$$

$$= \quad \mathbf{14.0}$$

30 The mean is greater than the mode.

31 (i) The additive model assumes $A = T + S$

   where $\quad A \; = \;$ actual

   $\qquad\qquad T \; = \;$ trend

   $\qquad\qquad S \; = \;$ seasonal variation

   Hence

   $A \; = \; (550 + 2.67 \times 12) + 52.8$

   $\; = \; \mathbf{635}$

   (ii) The multiplicative model assumes $A = T \times S$

   Hence

   $A \; = \; (550 + 2.67 \times 14) \times 0.76$

   $\; = \; \mathbf{446}$

32 Using the formula:

$b \quad = \quad \dfrac{n \sum xy - (\sum x)(\sum y)}{n \sum x^2 - (\sum x)^2}$

$ \quad = \quad \dfrac{12 \times 4,860 - 86 \times 48}{12 \times 3,364 - (86)^2}$

$ \quad = \quad \dfrac{54,192}{32,972}$

$ \quad = \quad \mathbf{1.644}$ to three decimal places

33   The coefficient of determination measures how much of the variation in the dependent variable is explained by the variation of the independent variable.

Thus $r^2 = (0.78)^2 = \textbf{60.8\%}$ to one decimal place.

34 $\dfrac{1+2+5}{100} = \dfrac{8}{100}$ contain faults.

Therefore $\dfrac{92}{100}$ or **0.92** are fault free.

35   £15.60 $(1.04)^5 = \textbf{£18.98}$